ENGLISH EMBROIDERY

ENGLISH EMBROIDERY

Sixteenth to Eighteenth Centuries

by Katharine B. Brett

Collections of the
Royal Ontario Museum

Crewelwork valance worked almost entirely
in satin stitch. 18th century, first half.
See page 57.

Contents

Colour Plates

2

ENGLISH EMBROIDERY
in the Royal Ontario Museum

The English embroideries in the Royal Ontario Museum are a delight to the eye and an inspiration for the embroidress. Those described here date from the second half of the 16th to the end of the 18th century and many styles and types are represented in the collection. The earliest is a rare black work pillow cover of the Tudor period. Next in date are costume accessories— a charming woman's coif and a pair of richly worked gloves with matching purse. Seventeenth century embroideries include several typical samplers, and half a dozen pictures. All tell something of the different stitches and techniques employed. Also of 17th century workmanship are an embroidered casket and a looking glass. Late 17th and early

18th century embroidery is best represented in the interesting and varied group of crewelwork bedcurtains and coverlets. The earliest in the group is a curtain dated 1696 and the most complete a set of bed curtains and valances with an unusual branching holly design.

The collection of 18th century silk embroideries contains several costume items including a group of short decorative aprons of the first half of the century and a dress of about 1740. The skill of the professional embroiderer is also represented in a beautiful satin coverlet worked with coloured silks and several kinds of silver and silver-gilt threads. Other costume items are in white work. There is a very fine petticoat worked entirely in back stitch, a man's waistcoat similarly worked, a delicate sleeve flounce of the early years of the century and a long apron of the late 18th century.

The embroideries have been divided, partly chronologically and partly by technique, into seven groups, each with a brief introductory survey followed by a description of each piece. No attempt has been made to cover areas in the field of English embroidery not contained in the collection.

Design: Scott Thornley, ROM
Photography: Leighton Warren
Chief Photographer, ROM
The text is set in ten point Palatino Roman
and printed on 80 pound Georgian Smooth
stock by The Hunter Rose Company
Limited, Toronto.

Strawberries, from a set of thirteen floral slips.
Early 17th century; see page 7.

Tudor Embroidery

The history of English embroidery is a long one but, with the exception of the great mediaeval period of ecclesiastical embroidery, we are almost entirely dependent on documentary evidence, rather than actual examples, for information about the different kinds that were done before the Reformation. The picture is far from complete up to the Tudor period. Portraits of the first half of the 16th century show richly embroidered garments and inventories reveal quantities of embroidered household articles. Records of the contents of Hampton Court, the palace of Henry VIII's Cardinal Wolsey, for instance, include two hundred embroidered bed hangings[1] but all these and much other domestic embroidery have now vanished.

One of the most familiar kinds of embroidery associated with the Tudor period is *black work*, embroidered with black silk on a linen ground. Examples in contemporary English portraits trim shirt collars, fronts and sleeve frills with patterns comparable in their linear style to those found in certain Continental monotone embroideries. When embroidery quite literally flowered in England under the more settled reign of Elizabeth I, blackwork, as well as that worked with coloured silks, acquired a completely English character. Roses, pansies, honeysuckle, carnations and other garden favourites entwined with coiling stems were worked in allover patterns, sometimes enhanced with metal threads and even peacock feathers, on jackets, hoods, coifs, purses, and caps as well as pillow covers, small cushions and coverlets, and many other articles of clothing and furnishings. The example of black work in Plate 1 shows a more geometric style with flowers and birds enclosed within a lattice.

Canvas work also flourished in the Tudor period. Valances and table carpets worked in tent stitch gave colour to the sparsely furnished rooms, and cushions with embroidered and tasselled covers provided comfort as well as an appearance of luxury to hard wooden stools and benches. Large articles such as bedcurtains, coverlets, and sometimes hangings of silk or wool were adorned with applied emblematic motifs or flower sprigs, called "slips," worked on canvas in tent stitch. These continued to be made during the first half of the 17th century, and because they were sturdy they outlasted the original fabric to which they were applied and could be remounted on new material. They were also less time consuming to embroider than were entire curtains and coverlets.

Gloves, accessories of dress of the Tudor and Stuart periods, displayed the skill of both the amateur embroidress and the professional. Because they were often worked as gifts they were therefore treasured possessions, and many examples have survived. Richly embroidered and perfumed gloves were a highly acceptable gift to Queen Elizabeth and a number are associated with her name. The pair shown in Plate 4 worked solidly with metal threads, seed pearls and a scattering of garnets is, with its matching purse, a sumptuous example of a 17th century style. Each gauntlet has two pockets for scent bags.

[1] M. A. Jourdain, *English Secular Embroidery*. London, 1910, p. 24.

1. Pillow Cover

16th century, second half
Acc. no. 923.4.73. Neg. no. 61T103
Formerly in the collection of Louisa,
Marchioness of Waterford
L. 48 cm, W. 75 cm

White linen tabby embroidered with
black silk floss and silver gilt filé over a pale
yellow silk core in double knot, running,
plaited braid, chain, interlaced four-legged
knot stitch, detached buttonhole, stem,
Holbein stitches, silver gilt spangles[1].

The lattice, with large rosettes at the
intersections, encloses alternate rows of birds
and flowers. The design is complete at the top
and sides but a little is missing across the
bottom. The birds are a turkey, a crane with
a fish in its mouth, a dove with an olive
branch and a phoenix rising from flames.
They symbolize the four elements earth,
water, air and fire[2]. Only one flower is
recognisable, the carnation. The others are
stylized and fanciful forms drawn from pattern books or derived from contemporary
silks.

Decorative pillow covers such as this
one and called "pillow beres," were intended
only for display and served no practical purpose except as a decorative embroidery in
the home.

Published:
Margaret Jourdain, *English Secular Embroidery,*
p. 142
Lady M. Alford, *Needlework as Art.* 1886. Pl. 82.
K. B. Brett, English Embroideries in Canada,
Embroidery, Volume XIII, no. 3, Autumn 1962
pp. 72-75.
Exhibited:
Det Danske Kunstindustremuseet,
Copenhagen, February, 1964.

---

[1] Cross and double cross stitch have been
worked with silver gilt filé into adjoining
silk stitches and silver gilt filé has been
intertwined with them as in basketry to
form discs.
[2] I am grateful to my colleague Mr. Donald
King for this suggestion.

2. Set of Thirteen Slips
Early 17th century
Acc. no. 928.14.1-13. Neg. no. 71TEX104-107
Average L. 22.2 cm, W. 19 cm

Worked on loosely woven linen tabby with floss silk in tent stitch. The recognisable plants in these slips are red and white strawberries, rose, carnation, marigold, periwinkle, pansy, lily, columbine, and mallow, but in most instances the foliage is not that of the plant depicted. The stumpy terminal is a characteristic of 17th century plants in embroidery[1].

Some pieces have a selvage down one side which has a pair of blue warps in it. All are hemmed and this was done before the embroidery was begun since one, worked on the 'wrong' side, has a drawing of a quite different plant on the right side.

---

[1] See *Commonplace Book*, manuscript by Thomas Trevelyon, London 1608, in the Folger Library, Washington, D. C. and for a later version Plate 24.

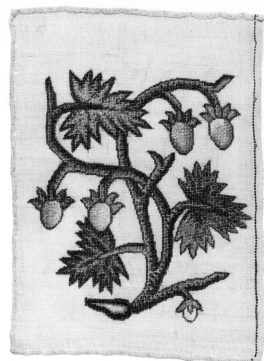

3. Coif
Late 16th-early 17th century
Acc. no. 930.13.1. Neg. no. 71TEX30

     Linen tabby embroidered with coloured 2-ply silks and silver filé in surface satin, French knots, laid and couched work, silver spangles.

     The pattern of flowers on coiling stems has been designed to fit the shape of the coif which has a drawstring around the neck.

     This piece is rare because it is a modest example of a woman's housecap of the period. The embroidery is skimpy compared with many richly worked examples which have survived and is worked mostly in surface satin stitch to allow most of the silk to appear on the surface.

9

4. Pair of Gloves with Matching Purse

17th century, first half
Acc. no. 947.60.1 a & b and .2.
Neg. no. ROMA201.7
Gift of Mr. Robert Stark
Gloves L. 37.5 cm
Purse 12.7 cm square

Linen 2/1 twill embroidered with yellow silk, silver and silver gilt filé over a light brown silk core, silver frisé over a linen core, and silver purl in laid and couched work, raised satin and stem stitches; seed pearls and garnets.

The embroidery on the cuffs is worked solidly and entirely conceals the linen ground. The glove and purse have the same arcading in laid work, and small birds worked with seed pearls, but the gloves also have winged dragons and, in the centre, a conical motif suggesting a bishop's mitre. This motif is also applied in each corner to form pockets for scent bags. The purse has curving leafy stems, small seed pearl flowers and two large fruits resembling pomegranates. The gloves are edged with silver bobbin laces decorated with spangles and the purse has tasselled draw strings and four tassels across the bottom.

The name of Mary Queen of Scots was traditionally associated with this set but the size and shape of the gauntlet cuffs suggest a later date. The style continued well into the 17th century.

Published:
K. B. Brett, English Embroideries in Canada, *Embroidery,* Volume XIII, no. 3, Autumn, 1962, pp. 72-75.

5. Small Panel
Late 16th to early 17th century
Acc. no. 926.39.6. Neg. no. 71TEX92
L.21.3 cm, W. 16.8 cm

Fine white linen tabby worked with pink and green floss silk in chain and trellis stitches, silver spangles held with 2-ply yellow silk.

The drawing of the spiralling pattern of green stems bearing oval pink fruits is complete, with a line around the edge, but the embroidery has not been finished. It is not known for what purpose this small panel was made, but it could serve as the top of a pincushion.

11

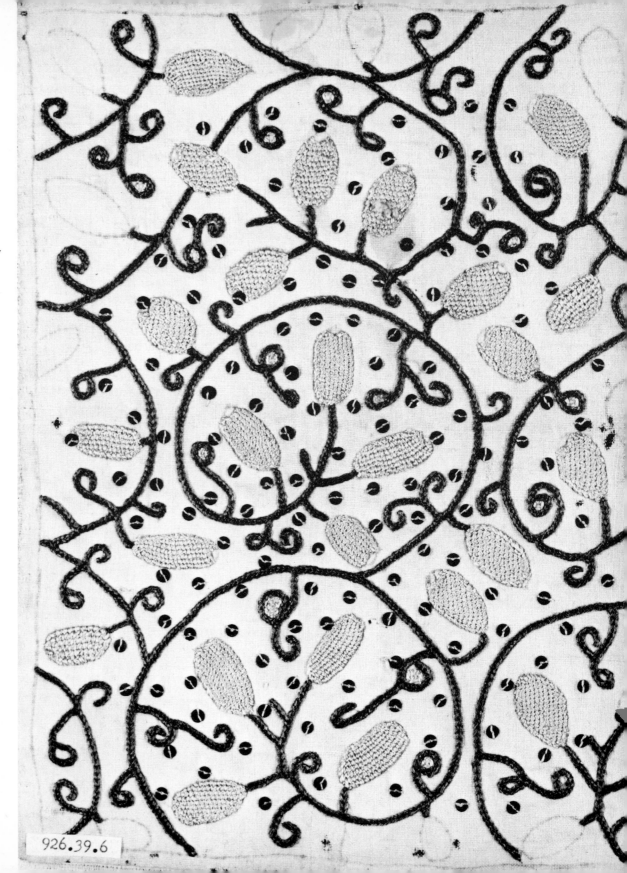

926.39.6

Mid 17th century spot sampler records motifs and repeating designs intended for borders and allover patterns. See page 14.

Samplers

Among the most treasured possessions in many homes today are samplers worked by forbears at a tender age or picked up as collectors' items. The 17th century spot motifs and neat rows of patterns, alphabets, and numerals worked with such care and precision, the gay little pictorial designs so characteristic of the 18th century sampler, surrounding dismal verses and inscriptions, and the child's name and often her age (usually under ten years) conjure up vivid pictures of wee mites intent upon their lessons in stitchery. It is thanks to proud parents and descendants that many samplers have survived.

Samplers, the name shortened from *exampler,* were not always a task for the young but, as the name implies, served another useful purpose. They were a file of patterns, collected by embroidresses from pattern books and from their friends, for future reference when planning embroidery projects for house furnishings and costume trimming, and so could be added to from time to time throughout a lifetime. Sixteenth century references suggest this purpose and so does the fact that samplers were often bequeathed. The earliest dated English sampler, 1598(1), is a mass of different patterns worked in a wide range of stitches and with little thought of an orderly arrangement such as is found in later examples. Early samplers are long and narrow but occasionally they were worked horizontally. The many kinds of flora and fauna which appear on them were intended to be copied on a larger scale for "slips" to apply to curtains and coverlets or incorporated into patterns for other purposes. Many occur in embroidered pictures and on the small square purses characteristic of the period.

The samples of complex diaper patterns, sometimes partly worked with metal threads, were intended for allover patterns for cushion covers and other household articles such as table carpets. The spot sampler shown on Plate 6 is a typical example. The fine, precise embroidery on this piece suggests that it was worked by an experienced hand.

Another 17th century type is the long, narrow band sampler which, as the name implies, was worked with rows of band or border patterns extending the width of the sampler. The band sampler was popular from the second quarter of the 17th century to the first quarter of the 18th century, but can be considered the typical sampler style of the second half of the 17th century. The bands are both wide and narrow and the same patterns, with variations, occur over and over again. The lack of originality and the fact that the patterns hardly ever reflected those in contemporary embroidery suggest a change in the sampler's purpose. It was no longer a record of patterns but had become a school exercise. It is relevant that alphabets and, later, numerals first occur in band samplers. Many a small child must have learned her letters and numerals as she worked her sampler. Names and dates frequently follow the alphabet but rarely go beyond initials in spot samplers. Skill in embroidering letters and numerals was essential for marking the quantities of household linen possessed by many families. The large alphabets worked in eyelet stitch would have been suitable for heavy materials such as blankets.

Seventeenth century samplers embroidered in cut, drawn, and white work are related to band samplers in arrangement. Many of them display remarkable skill with the needle; some cut and drawn thread designs are so complex as to suggest that they may be lacemakers' samples. That they were certainly needlework tasks for the young is recorded in the progress of Martha Edlin who worked her sampler with coloured silks in 1668, at the age of eight, and completed her white work sampler the following year.

Long, narrow samplers continued to be made in the first half of the 18th century, but a wide rectangular shape is typical of the period. Bands of patterns also lingered on but the sampler was, by the second quarter of the century, changing from what must have been a tedious exercise, to a picture to be displayed. A verse, a biblical quotation, or an inscription, usually expressing sombre thoughts about life and death, formed the focal point in the centre. The verse *On Youth* worked on the sampler in Plate 16 contains a comparatively gentle warning.

When Spring appears and Violets blow
And shed a rich perfume
How soon the Fragrance breathes its last
How short liv'd is the Bloom
Such are the charms that flush the Cheek
And Sparkle in the Eye
So soon the lovely Finishd Form
The Transient graces Fly

The verses were surrounded by a contrastingly gay array of floral motifs, birds, and beasts, and finished with a border all round. This became the accepted arrangement as the century advanced. These samplers were almost always done by children. Names and dates, or names and ages, completed the exercise which was then framed and proudly displayed. Many 18th century samplers were worked on narrow wool tabby with blue threads in the selvages and called tammy cloth. The narrow width suggests that tammy may have been made especially for samplers but could well serve for other purposes such as linings. Tammies, not necessarily all of narrow width, were made in the midlands and north of England and in Scotland[2]. Samplers were still worked in a number of different stitches but they were chosen to suit the motifs and not because they were essential to learning embroidery. Satin and cross stitches occur most frequently.

White work samplers of this century illustrate changes in lacy patterns. Cut and drawn work, no longer in fashion although they still appeared on samplers, had given way to fine patterned "hollie" point fillings intended for the crowns of baby bonnets. The Museum's example Plate 13, dated 1734 is one of several small square ones of about the same period with almost identical arrangements of rows of "hollie" point, each including a square of cut and drawn thread work.

During the last two decades of the 18th century map samplers were enormously popular, if one may judge from the number that have survived. They first appeared earlier in the century but most of them are dated in the 1780s and 1790s. They were no doubt a form of geography lesson to teach children the counties of Britain and the countries of Europe.

---

[1] Patricia Wardle. *Guide to English Embroidery.* Victoria and Albert Museum, 1970, cat. no. 38.

[2] I am grateful to my colleague Mr. Donald King, of the Victoria and Albert Museum for this information.

6. Spot Sampler
Mid 17th century
Acc. no. 960.126.1. Neg. no. 60AA48
L.58.4 cm, W. 32 cm

Loosely woven linen tabby worked with coloured 2-ply silks, silver and silver gilt filé over a pale yellow silk core in plaited braid, rococo, back, eyelet, plaited and encroaching Gobelin, tent and Florentine stitches.

The motifs include a number of birds, beasts and insects including two rabbits, a squirrel, a hound, a parrot, a butterfly and a snail. There is also a rose, a marigold, a pansy and a number of repeating designs intended for borders and allover patterns. Silks are frequently used double and the selvages across the top and bottom have a pair of blue warps in them and a 2-ply blue warp at the edge.

This is a typical example of the long narrow 17th century spot sampler. Occasionally they are worked horizontally.
Published:
K. B. Brett, English Embroideries in Canada, *Embroidery,* Volume XIII, No. 3, Autumn 1962, pp. 72-75.

7. **Band Sampler**
Mid 17th century
Acc. no. 962.25.1. Neg. no. 62AA217
L. 62.2 cm, W. 19 cm

White linen tabby worked with green, blue, grey, pink and cream 2-ply silk in running, double running, Holbein, trellis, Algerian eye, and two sided Italian cross stitches.

The sampler has eight bands of pattern including a variant of the "boxer" motif[1] and two allover geometric patterns. Part of a line of letters shows at the top which is incomplete. There is a simple selvage across the bottom.

There are many variants of this kind of sampler with similar and sometimes almost identical patterned bands. They are not always samplers in the true sense but often served as school exercises. They rarely have either the wide range of stitches or subject matter that spot samplers have, and are more highly organized. The earliest dated one is 1629[2] and has the same rose and acorn pattern as in the wide band near the top of this one.

---

[1] See Donald King. Boxers. *Embroidery*, Volume XII, no. 4, Winter 1961-62, pp. 114-115.
[2] See Averil Colby, *Samplers*, fig. 56.

15

8. Band Sampler. 1672
Acc. no. 962.207. Neg. no. 71TEX20
L. 51.4 cm, W. 18.7 cm

White linen tabby worked with green, brown, yellow and white 2-ply silk and white linen in Gobelin, Algerian eye, marking cross, Montenegrin cross, Holbein, and double running stitches.

There are seven border patterns on this sampler including a variant of the "boxer" motif and, across the bottom, two alphabets. One is in silks, the other in linen above the signature MARY CARON in eyelet work and the date 1672.

Once samplers became a school exercise they were often used as a device to teach alphabet and numerals and these appear on band samplers with increasing frequency from the mid 17th century on. The band patterns continue to be variants of those found in earlier samplers. This one has a variant of the rose and acorn pattern and "boxer" motif seen in Plate 7.

9. White Work Sampler
17th century, second half
Acc. no. 962.25.2. Neg. no. 62AA217
L. 60.3 cm, W. 19 cm

White linen tabby embroidered with linen thread in cut and drawn work. French knots, needle lace fillings, and double hemstitch.

There are many short bands of geometric patterns mostly in cut and drawn work, and two short samples of needlepoint lace edging are worked part way down the right edge. The sampler has been cut off at the bottom.

10. Sampler
17th century, second half
Acc. no. 962.133.1. Neg. no. 62AA217
Gift of Mrs. Anne Ellis
L. 56.5 cm, W. 194 cm

White linen tabby worked with linen thread in cut and drawn work, Algerian eye, double hem, needle lace fillings, and geometrical satin stitches.

Across the top are several narrow bands of geometric patterns and between them a wide floral band all worked in geometric satin stitch. Two alphabets follow: the first, in satin stitch, includes the name JANE USBORNE. The second is in eyelet work. There are four bands of cut work with needle point fillings across the centre. The rest of the sampler is incomplete.

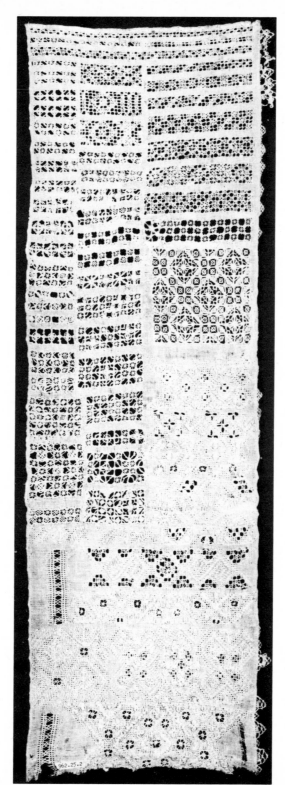

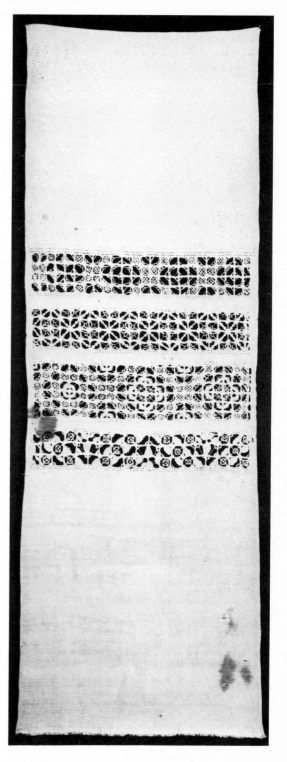

11. Long Sampler. 1673
Acc. no. 941.12.2. Neg. no. 71TEX19
Gift of Mrs. H. A. Thompson
L. 44.7 cm, W. 16.8 cm

Fine linen tabby embroidered with coloured wools and a little linen in Holbein, satin, buttonhole filling, Montenegrin cross and double running stitches.

There are nine band patterns all with stylized floral patterns and at the bottom an alphabet followed by the maker's name and the date, DORCAS TANNER EZEKIEL 1673. There is a selvage across the bottom.

Samplers of this period worked in wool are less common than those worked with coloured silks. They suffered the depredations of moth and mildew as in this example and have long since vanished. This one has several variants of the rose and oak leaf pattern including a wide one very similar to that in Plate 7 but including strawberries. Only the name, date and border patterns across the bottom are worked in linen and may not be original.

12. Long Sampler. 1719
Acc. no. 964.104. Neg. no. 71TEX20
L. 45.1 cm, W. 19.7 cm

Loosely woven linen tabby embroidered with blue, yellow, green, cream and and pink 2-ply and singles silk in geometrical satin, Algerian eye, Montenegrin cross, marking cross, and double running stitches.

There are three narrow border patterns across the top followed by an alphabet ending with the words & MaRY BReWer. Another alphabet follows ending & MaRY. An inscription comes next reading THINK OF Me WHeN YOU See ME NOT SPeaK OF Me as YOU FINDe FOR I aM NOT LIKe The WeaTHeR COCK THaT CHanGeTH aT EVeRY WIND and below this WITH CaRe aND PaINS HaVe I ThIS WROUGHT aND ENDeD IT WITH A VIRGINS ThOUGHT. M BReWeR. At the bottom below a border pattern of crosses is the date FeBRUARY The 28 1719 and a narrow border pattern. Selvages at top and bottom.

Texts, numbers, quotations and personal comments followed on the heels of alphabets and numbers in samplers of the second half of the 17th century and were an established part of the sampler repertoire in the 18th century. This one is almost entirely filled with lettering and has only narrow border patterns between each line.

_____

[1] See Averil Colby, _Samplers_, fig. 105.

13. Square Sampler. 1734
Acc. no. 967.293. Neg. no. 71TEX93
Gift of Mr. Gordon C. Miller
L. 21 cm, W. 14.9 cm

Fine white linen tabby embroidered with yellow silk and white linen thread in geometrical satin, cutwork, hollie, needlepoint lace and back stitches.

Three rows of squares filled with needlepoint and "hollie" point patterns have a row between them of small circles with patterns in the same stitches. To the left of the two central needlepoint squares is one with a parrot in "hollie" point. The one at the right is inscribed MARTHE ARRON 1734.

This is one of a group of samplers all dated about the same period [1] and may have been a standard type of open work sampler at that time.

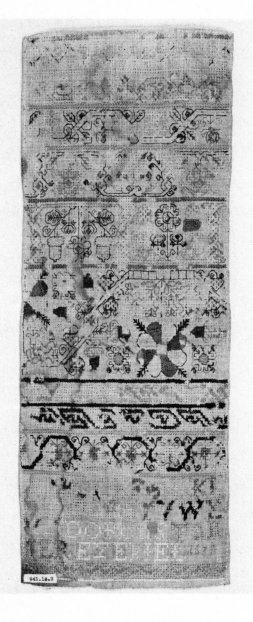

14. Long Sampler. 1737
Acc. no. 968.203.3. Neg. no. 71TEX17
Gift of Mrs. Duncan Graham
L. 39.4 cm, W. 19.1 cm

Loosely woven natural linen tabby worked with red and green 2-ply wool in cross, Algerian eye, rococo, Holbein, double running, and crosslet stitches.

Most of the top half is filled by six border patterns and the remainder by an upper and a lower case alphabet, the numbers one to seven and a large eyelet-work alphabet. Across the bottom are the initials KH and JUN 9 x JULY 21'737. There are selvages at the top and bottom.

Satin, cross and four-sided stitches were the earliest stitches used for alphabets and they were soon followed by eyelet stitches. Alphabets in this stitch were always much larger than in the other stitches and may have been useful for marking heavy fabrics since the purpose of alphabets and numbers in samplers was not only to learn letters and numerals but also for marking the vast quantities of linens required by a large household. The letters I and U were usually left out and, in the 17th century Q was often written ꟼ as in this sampler which is old fashioned in style.

It is unusual to find the starting date as well as the finishing date on samplers.

15. Long Sampler. 1746
Acc. no. 970.202.19. Neg. no. 71TEX17
L. 53 cm, W. 20 cm

Loosely woven tabby linen worked with coloured 2-ply wools in cross, Algerian eye, rococo, and double back stitches.

There are two wide and two narrow band patterns with an alphabet and part of another between them. The vowels *a e i o u* follow the complete alphabet. Across the lower part is worked yet another part alphabet and the inscription *Glory be to The Father & to The Son and to the holy Ghost* followed by numerals 1 to 23. Below this is part of an alphabet from A to R in eyelet work and, at the bottom, Dorothy PoWel her SaM Cloth Aged 11 In the Year Of Our Lord 1746 I PM. There are selvages at top and bottom.

The wide border across the centre is primitive in style and is not from the usual repertoire of sampler patterns. It may have been designed by Dorothy Powel herself. Another feature is the inclusion of the five vowels—another example of the sampler as a means of teaching.

16. Sampler. 1787
Acc. no. 954.26. Neg. no. 71TEX22
Gift of Mrs. C. M. Thompson
L. 45.1 cm, W. 32 cm

Worsted tabby called tammy cloth embroidered with coloured 2-ply silks in cross, and geometrical satin stitches.

At the top there are pots of flowers and small birds, and there are more small plants and birds at the bottom. A floral border runs around all four sides and in the centre a verse entitled ON YOUTH (See p.13). Below a zigzag border are the following lines:
See how the lilies flourish White and fair see how the ravens fed from heaven are then ne'er distrust thy God for cloth and bread Whilst lilies flourish and ravens fed(1).
A medallion at the bottom encloses the name and age of the maker and the date: REBECCAH CHILMAN HER WORK AGED 8 YEARS MARCH THE 30 1787.

The wide rectangular form is characteristic of the 18th century sampler and the plan of this one is typical of those where verses framed by flowery borders were the main feature. Most of the verses have a high moral tone and the majority must have been painfully sad and discouraging to the little girls who worked them. This one on the fleetingness of youth is cheerful compared with those that warned against life's brief and dreary span and recommended preparation for the life hereafter.

Tammy cloth, a loosely woven worsted tabby, became an alternate to linen in the 18th century. It was made in narrow widths averaging about twelve and a half inches and is thought to have been made especially for samplers.

---

(1) Samplers with this short verse and others with similar themes have been classified as Easter samplers by Marcus Huish and certainly in this instance there are grounds for such a suggestion since Easter fell on April 8 in 1787.

21

17. Sampler. 1789
Acc. no. 958.108.8. Neg. no. 71 TEX36
Gift of the Estate of Miss Mary Rolph
L. 45.7 cm, W. 32.3 cm

Worsted tammy cloth embroidered with coloured 2-ply silks in cross, stem, herringbone, Holbein, and satin, geometrical and encroaching satin stitches.

A meander floral border runs around the edge and there is a band pattern distantly related to some found in 17th century band samplers across the top. Below this is a floral wreath surrounding the biblical text, PROVERBS CHAP XXXI *30 Favour is deceitful and beauty is vain but a woman that feareth the LORD she shall be praised JEAN THOMSON sowd this sempler in the year 1789.* On either side is a small rectangle; that on the left bears the name RICHARD THOMSON and that on the right ELIZABETH AUCHINCLOS, perhaps the names of the embroidress's parents. The former is worked in coloured silk, the latter with black silk. Presumably the mother was deceased. At the bottom of the sampler Adam and Eve stand under a fruiting tree with a bird in the centre and the snake twined around the trunk. There are selvages at the sides with four blue warps at the edges and two further in.

22

18. **Square Sampler.** 1796
Acc. no. 952.12. Neg. no. 71TEX23
Gift of Miss E. M. Brown
31.1 cm square

Worsted tammy cloth embroidered with coloured 2-ply silks in Algerian eye and cross stitches.

There are four alphabets alternating with three sets of numerals across the upper part. The top ones are double with two of each letter and numeral side by side. At the bottom, between two vases of pink flowers, there is a verse entitled FRIENDSHIP.

Tell me, ye knowing and discerning few,
Where I may find a Friend both firm and true
Who dares stand by me when in deep Distress,
And then his Love and Friendship most express.

The name, age of the maker, and the date are worked below: *Elizabeth Carter Finish'd her work In the eighth year Of her age 1796.* The selvages at the sides have four blue warps at the edge and a pair further in.

The alphabets in this sampler have both I and J and, further on, V and U in that order.

23

19. Sampler. 1797

Acc. no. 958.108.7. Neg. no. 71TEX36
Gift of Estate of Miss Mary Rolph
L. 44.1 cm, W. 32.4 cm

Worsted tammy cloth embroidered with coloured 2-ply silks in satin, geometrical and encroaching satin, cross, stem, and chain stitches.

A meander floral border surrounds the design which has a band across the top distantly related to some in 17th century samplers. Below this, within a floral wreath is a biblical quotation, PROVERBS CHAP XXXI *10 who can find a virtuous woman for her price is far above rubies ELIZABETH THOMSON sewed this sampler in the year 1797*. There is a stone house flanked by fruiting trees in the centre and a straight path leading from it to a grassy plot in the foreground with small animals on it and a cow on either side. There are many small floral motifs interspersed throughout the design. The selvages at the sides are the same as those in Plate 17.

Houses, probably the homes of the young embroidresses, are a favourite subject in 18th century samplers. They are usually within a garden setting which provides a reason for filling every available space with flowers, beasts and birds.

The band across the top, the floral wreath, and some of the flower sprays are almost identical to those in Jean Thomson's sampler though worked in different stitches and colours. The surrounding border is a variant of that in the Jean Thomson sampler. The two girls were probably related, perhaps stepsisters or cousins.

24

20. **Map Sampler.** 1783
Acc. no. 956.21.1. Neg. no. 71TEX28
Gift of Miss C. W. Johnson
L. 67.3 cm, W. 63.5 cm

Loosely woven linen tabby embroidered with coloured silks in cross stitch.

The map shows England and Wales with part of Scotland at the top and Flanders and France in the lower right corner. A floral wreath in the upper right corner encloses the inscription *MAP of ENGLAND Work'd By Elizabeth Harriot Gilley In The Year of our LORD One Thousand Seven Hundred And Eighty Three and In The Eleventh Year of Her Age.* There is a selvage down the right side.

In this example of the map sampler not only are the names of the countries shown but also as many place names as can be fitted into each.

21. **Map Sampler**
Late 18th century. 1780-1795
Acc. no. 970.118.1. Neg. no. 71TEX29
Gift of Mr. and Mrs. Harold B. Burnham
L. 54.6 cm, W. 53.3 cm

Worsted tammy cloth worked with coloured silks in stem and cross stitches.

The map shows the continent of Europe. Each country is outlined with rows of stem stitch in three colours, one of which is always black. The names of countries and some place names are shown. A small floral wreath in the upper left corner bears the inscription *A Map of Europe by Sarah Walker*. There are selvages, with three blue warps at the edge and two further in, at each side.

22. **Map Sampler**
Late 18th century
Acc. no. 958.108.1. Neg. no. 71TEX97
Estate of Miss Mary Rolph
L. 36.8 cm, W. 34.3 cm

Worsted tammy cloth embroidered with coloured 2-ply silks in stem and cross and geometrical satin stitches.

This map of England and Wales has all the counties outlined with several rows of stem stitch. There are no place names, other than the counties, except around the coast. In the upper right corner a scalloped medallion contains the inscription *A Map of England & Wales by Charlt Moore*.

Embroidered picture (mid 17th century)
includes motifs in raised work. See page 28.

Pictures, Caskets and Looking Glasses

Pictures are perhaps the most charming examples of embroidery associated with 17th century England and those with small figures, standing on little mounds amid enormous flora and fauna and dating from the second and third quarters of the century, are the most familiar. They were often embroidered by young girls and the standard of workmanship varies in consequence. Some are worked directly on a satin ground on which the design has first been drawn, others are composed of various kinds of applied work, both flat and raised. The embroidery is worked with coloured silks and sometimes several kinds of metal and twisted silk threads are employed. In their efforts to produce realistic effects the embroidresses' ingenuity is often quite extraordinary. Plate 23 is an interesting example of elaborate applied work. Plates 24 and 25, on the other hand, illustrate simpler forms of the technique. Both the latter two are worked mostly in tent stitch but one is flat and the other raised by padding. All manner of odds and ends must have been used for padding, including wool wadding and short lengths of leftover silk threads. The flowers, birds, and beasts worked on spot samplers often appear on a larger scale in these pictures.

Many pictures were worked entirely in tent stitch on linen canvas with coloured wools and silks and depict figure groups, sometimes drawn from engravings illustrating biblical stories, Ovid's *Metamorphoses*, the four seasons, the five senses or allegorical subjects. They are usually embroidered against landscape settings of rolling hillocks. This scheme is echoed in the idyllic scenes in embroidered pictures of the first half of the 18th century. A favourite subject of that period was a shepherdess sitting beneath a tree with her flock grazing nearby; another was a bouquet of flowers. The same subjects also occur on screens, chair covers, and dress accessories such as purses.

The taste for embroidered pictures declined in the 1740s but was revived again at the end of the century in quite different styles. Again the subject matter was idyllic but it was worked on silk with coloured silks and sometimes chenille. Often only the figures and landscape were embroidered, and the sky and faces painted in. This kind of picture embroidery continued into the early 19th century. Another fashion in embroidered pictures was that of copying, almost to the last line of detail, engravings of stately homes and architectural landmarks. They were worked with black silk and embroidered to simulate the lines and textures of engraving and aquatints.

Caskets and boxes of the mid 17th century, which served various purposes, were often entirely covered with embroidery in the flat and raised work styles of contemporary pictures, and like them were projects for the young. After she had finished her two samplers[1], Martha Edlin went on to embroider panels to cover a casket. Pieces drawn to fit the side, top, door, and drawer front surfaces were often professionally prepared and, when the embroidery was completed, professionally applied. The subject matter of the patterns followed the same range as that for pictures. Those on the Museum's casket, for instance, are taken from the Old Testament. Looking glass frames, sometimes of tortoise shell, were also elaborately inset with embroidered panels similar to those on caskets and boxes but the subject matter is often that of a man and a woman, and large flower sprigs, like those on the little looking glass in Plate 35.

---

[1] See page 13. Her work may be seen in the Victoria and Albert Museum.

23. Picture
Mid 17th century
Acc. no. 932.15. Neg. no. 71TEX83
L. 25.4 cm, W. 34.9 cm

White satin embroidered with coloured silks, linen, silver frise over silk cores of several colours, silver filé over a white silk core, silver purl and lamella, looped and flattened silver wires, and chenille in split, detached buttonhole, back, wave, satin, long and short stitches, laid and couched work, spangles.

The figures of a man and a woman stand under a canopy in the centre. At the right the sun comes out from under a cloud above a domed house with a figure standing in the open doorway. Below this is a saddled and bridled horse above a pool in the lower corner. On the left is a pear tree and below it a pea pod which appears to be growing from a fountain pool in the lower corner. Water flows into the pool from a mask. The picture has been mounted on silk and has a border of silver bobbin lace.

Most of the motifs are in raised work or have been worked separately and only partly applied as, for instance, the canopy and the costumes of the figures under it. In some parts the silk cores of the metal threads have been painted.

24. Picture

Mid 17th century
Acc. no. 937.15.1. Neg. no. 71TEX63
Gift of Mrs. H. J. Cody
L. 38.7 cm, W. 50.8 cm

White satin embroidered with coloured silks and fine silk twisted on a wire core in tent, bullion, stem, brick, split, and couching stitches.

The figures of a man and a woman stand in the centre, the woman playing a lute. There is a plum tree between them and an iris and a carnation, a rose and tulip among the large "slip" plants around and above them. In the lower left corner a shepherd sits playing his flute under a pear tree. Three sheep, one of them black, stand nearby. A hound chases a hare across the bottom of the picture, watched by a leopard in the lower right corner. The intervening space around the central figures is filled with flowers, birds, and insects, a frog, a snail, and caterpillars, probably all drawn from pattern books.

This is a typical example of the 17th century embroidresses' delight in miscellaneous flora and fauna. Some are almost identical to those worked on the mid 17th century sampler, Plate 6.

29

25. Picture

17th century, third quarter
Acc. no. 937.15.2. Neg. no. 71TEX84
Gift of Mrs. H. J. Cody
L. 36.8 cm, W. 48 cm

White satin ground. Motifs worked on linen canvas with coloured silks in tent stitch and padded and applied with close couching over laid groups of silk floss threads.

An angel, holding a long horn in each hand, stands on a grassy bridge with a small boat below on rippling water. There is a little rabbit at her side, and above her, a house with wings on either side and a gated wall joining them across the front to form a courtyard. Other motifs are a peacock and a pheasant and, in each corner, a large flower sprig. All the flowers are fanciful except the iris in the lower right corner. There is either a snake, a snail, or a caterpillar crawling on the foliage of each. Insects fly here and there on the background.

26. Picture

17th century, third quarter
Acc. no. 961.153.2. Neg. no. 63AA545
L. 43.2 cm, W. 60.4 cm

White satin embroidered with coloured silks, silver frisé over a linen core, and purl in back, split, French knots, stem, long and short, tent, rococo and satin stitches, laid and couched work and detached buttonhole stitch and variations for raised parts. Short, close satin stitches have been cut to form a pile.

The scenes depicted are from the story of Pyramus and Thisbe. In the centre Thisbe mourns over the body of Pyramus prone beside the tomb of Ninus. A small figure of Cupid, sitting quietly by, is an added touch of sorrowing love. He does not come into the story in Ovid's *Metamorphoses.* On the other side of a central tree the lion tears at Thisbe's veil. In the lower right corner Thisbe emerges from the cave where she has been hiding from the lion. At the top right is a castle and just below are two figures under an oak tree and another pair at the left side. We can only surmise that they may be intended for Pyramus and Thisbe exchanging glances. Trees, flowers, birds, beasts and insects are interspersed among the scenes of the story. The figures, the castle, the cave, and some birds and beasts are in raised work, and many of the flowers and foliage have free-standing petals and leaves. The heads of the figures under the tree at the right are only drawn in. The unevenness of the embroidery of their garments around the neck suggests that the heads are unfinished.

Published:
K. B. Brett. English Embroideries in Canada, *Embroidery,* Volume XIII, No. 3, Autumn, 1962, pp. 72-75.

31

27. Picture

17th century, third quarter
Acc. no. 968.26.74. Neg. no. 71TEX99
Gift of The W. Garfield Weston
Charitable Foundation
L. 19.5 cm, W. 39 cm

White satin embroidered with coloured silks in bullion, satin, couching, French knot, and detached buttonhole stitches.

A man and a woman stand on low rolling hillocks with a large tulip between them and the sun coming from a cloud above. There are three striped tents in the upper left corner and a house with wings and tower and a gated wall across the front in the upper right. In the lower corners are a winged griffon and a winged and crested dragon.

28. Picture

Third quarter, 17th century
Acc. no. 963.108. Neg. no. 63AA545
L. 27.3 cm, W. 30.2 cm

Linen tabby embroidered with coloured silks in tent stitch and a few French knots.

The figure of a man and a woman are seated at a table under a flowering and fruiting tree, entwined with a grapevine. The table has a striped tablecloth on it and a plate. A monkey is perched on the back of the woman's chair and she feeds a dog beside her. The man holds a wine glass with a fly poised on the edge. A large caterpillar crawls up the back of his chair. Other motifs in the picture are a rose, a carnation, a pansy, a turkey, a frog, a snail, a large fly and another caterpillar.

There is no doubt, by the disposition of the animals and insects about the table, that the humour in this picture is quite intentional. The embroidery is on a fine scale, there being over 1700 stitches to the square inch.

29. Embroidered Picture
Early 18th century
Acc. no. 919.9.29. Neg. no. 71TEX32
L. 26.8 cm, W. 38.1 cm

Loosely woven linen tabby embroidered with coloured 2-ply silks in tent, cross, satin, geometrical satin, Roumanian, Hungarian, French knot, laid and couching stitches.

There is a female figure at the left seated under a flowering tree and holding an olive branch. Another female figure stands before her in Greek classical costume and with her right arm raised. A fox or wolf observes the scene from the lower right corner. Most of the right half of the picture is filled with a large castle with roofs, turrets and walls worked in several different stitches and patterns. The upper branches of the tree have been drawn but not embroidered. The drawing shows through the solid embroidery of the sky.

So great a variety of stitches is not often found in embroidery of this kind which is usually limited to cross and tent stitch. The scene may be one inspired by classical mythology.

919.9.29b

30. Picture. 1730
Acc. no. 941.6.172. Neg. no. 71TEX64
Gift of Mrs. Joseph Eaton Burnside
L. 48.2 cm, W. 44.5 cm

Linen canvas embroidered with coloured 2-ply wools, 2-ply silks and silk floss in tent, cross and geometrical satin stitch.

A shepherdess is depicted seated beneath an oak tree with a lamb on her knee which she is feeding with milk from a leather flask. A small flock of sheep and a dog are nearby. There is a pretentious red brick house in a distant hill, clouds in the sky, and several birds flying by. It is initialled EH and dated 1730. The sky is worked in a diaper pattern with pale yellow floss silk in satin stitch.

Shepherdesses abound in embroidered pictures and chair covers of the first half of the 18th century and are usually to be found sitting beneath a tree.

35

31. Picture

18th century, second quarter
Acc. no. 967.117.1. Neg. no. 68TEX113
Gift of Miss Lucile M. H. Hoskins
L. 34.3 cm, W. 33.7 cm

Linen canvas worked with coloured
2-ply wools and silks in tent stitch.

The figures of a man and woman,
wearing cloaks trimmed with miniver, are
seated in high-backed chairs in a landscape
setting. The woman holds a dog in her lap,
the man plays a pipe. At the left is a stone
balustrade and, between two trees, a
bird flies.

The picture is just as it came off the
embroidery frame, with tape stitched to the
edges of the canvas, and some sample
stitches worked on the left side.

32. Picture

About 1790
Acc. no. 969.109.2
Gift of Queen's University,
Kingston, Ontario
L. 39 cm, W. 31.5 cm

White silk tabby embroidered with
coloured silks and chenille in split, satin
and surface satin stitches.

The picture is oval and depicts a
woman sitting on the grass under a tree with
a child in her lap. Another woman stands
before her offering a dish containing a
bunch of grapes. Both women are dressed in
costume of the 1780s. The sky, faces, and
hands are painted.
Worked by Mrs. Galbraith of Darlington

36

33. Picture
Late 18th century
Acc. no. 927.27.6. Neg. no. 71TEX41
L. 45.5 cm, W. 66 cm

Firm white cotton tabby embroidered with black 2-ply silk in speckling stitches.

The black outline of Burghley House is only partly embroidered around the edges. The subject is from an at present unknown engraved source.

Many embroidered pictures of this kind were sheer tours de force. This one no doubt would have been one had it been completed. The tiny speckling stitches are worked to simulate mezzotint, aquatint, or stipple engraving.

34. Casket

17th century, third quarter
Acc. no. 960.149. Neg. no. 60AA51
H. 30.5 cm, W. 26.7 cm, D. 18.4 cm

White satin embroidered with
coloured silks in couching, long and short,
running and satin stitches.

Several scenes from Genesis are
depicted on this casket. On the top of the lid
is the scene of Isaac's servant leading his
camels and offering Rebekah the golden
bracelet. Jacob's dream is on the back of
the box, Abraham and the Angel of the Lord
on the left side and the meeting of Jacob and
Rachel on the right side. Isaac's servant with
camels is shown departing from Abraham
on the outside of the doors and Hagar and
Ishmael being cast forth on the inside. Other
areas on the outside are filled with rustic
scenes. Inside the doors, above two rows of
drawers, is the scene of the angel of the Lord
appearing to Hagar and Ishmael in the
wilderness. There are flowers on the row of
three small drawers and on the long drawer
below.

The high, angled, lid is a container;
the top is hinged. The casket itself has a
fixed tray divided into sections. Two are
fitted with glass bottles and one is a
pincushion.

35. Looking Glass

Mid 17th century
Acc. no. 949.14. Neg. no. ROMA4.49 and
71TEX85
L. 37.3 cm, W. 30 cm

White satin embroidered with
coloured silks in satin, split, long and short,
stem stitches, French knot, and couching;
spangles.

The figure of a man is embroidered
on the left door, and that of a woman on the
right. Both are surrounded by large flowers.
The frame is filled with flowers on a
spangled ground. Among them the tulip,
rose and carnation are recognisable. The
edges are bound with silver filé tape, the
doors lined with stamped pink silk and the
back covered with red velvet. The looking
glass can either stand on a table or hang on
the wall by a brass ring which is attached
to the back.

The frame is very simply worked
and may have been done by a young girl
following the completion of her samplers.
Published:
K. B. Brett, English Embroideries in Canada.
Embroidery, Volume XIII, no. 3, Autumn
1962, pp. 72-75.

39

36. Panel From a Looking Glass?
Mid 17th century
Acc. no. 968.26.75. Neg. no. 71TEX100
Gift of The W. Garfield Weston Charitable
Foundation
L. 15.5 cm, W. 36.6 cm

    White satin embroidered with
coloured silks in rococo, couching, split,
tent, stem, French knot, Florentine, long
and short, and detached buttonhole stitches.
    A woman in the centre holds a vase
of flowers in one hand and a bouquet in the
other. At her right side is a running river
with a fish in it. A church near a tree, and
other trees and flower sprigs, surround her,
and there is a large fanciful flower at either
end. A border of flowers, birds, beasts, and
insects is worked across the top.

37. Cushion

Mid 17th century
Acc. no. 960.126.2. Neg. no. 60AA49
L. 29.2 cm, W. 17.8 cm

White tabby silk embroidered with coloured silks, silver filé over a pale yellow silk core, purl and silver filé cord in stem, satin, long and short, chain, back, French knot, split stitches, laid and couched work; spangles.

The crowned figure in the centre, with banner inscribed PRAISE THE LORD YE ANGELS, may be intended for King David. He wears a cloak lined with miniver. On either side of him is an angel rising from highly stylized clouds. They have flames above their heads, and a draped canopy hangs from a thread over all three figures. They are framed by a narrow floral border. The blue silk damask on the back has Arabic inscriptions in the design. It is Syrian, probably 14th to 15th century[1].

The cushion is a hard one and probably served to support a bible. The solid couching called *or nué* employed in this piece was developed in Flanders[2]. It is usually the work of a professional embroiderer of heraldic and ecclesiastical articles. The backing may be a piece from a vestment. Many vestments were cut up and used for other purposes after the Reformation.

Published:
K. B. Brett, English Embroideries in Canada, *Embroidery,* Volume XII, no. 3, Autumn 1962, pp. 72-75.

[1] An almost identical piece is illustrated in A. F. Kendrick *Catalogue of Mohammedan Textiles of the Mediaeval Period.* Victoria and Albert Museum. 1924, plate XIV.
[2] See Patricia Wardle *Guide to English Embroidery.* Victoria and Albert Museum, 1970, p. 14

Crewelwork bedcurtain, second quarter of the 18th century. See page 52.

Crewelwork

One of the showiest kinds of English embroidery is that called crewelwork, with designs worked with coloured long staple worsted yarns called crewels, on a firm twill fabric with a linen warp and cotton weft. A 2/1 twill most frequently occurs but there are examples with chevron and a fancy twill in this collection. In most instances the soft cotton weft almost entirely hides the firm linen warp. This material of mixed yarns first appears in English embroidery about the middle of the 17th century[1] and coincides with the rise of the importation into Europe of cotton of many kinds, both yarns and fabrics, from India, and raw cotton from the Levant. Its strength and firmness was ideal for embroidered furnishings and the great majority of examples that have come down to us are bedcurtains.

An early example in the Victoria and Albert Museum[2] has the traditional style of repeating pattern with flowers enclosed within coiling stems but as the possibilities of crewelwork were explored by imaginative needlewomen and embroidery designers, new patterns appear. Some with leaf meanders seem to have soon been superseded by large branches usually growing on small hillocks with fanciful leaf forms derived from those in silk and laces[3] in the contemporary baroque style but transposed into a style all their own. One source of inspiration may have been the "practise of printing large branches for hangings for Romes" noted by the directors of the London East India Company writing to their agents in Surat in 1669. Nothing survives of this fashion nor is it certain whether they were textiles or wall papers, but there may be a link between the large printed branches and those of crewelwork since those in the latter sometimes not only repeat horizontally but also vertically. This is a device that is practical for printing, when blocks must be a manageable size and repeats are economical, but not necessary in embroidery. This practice is well illustrated in Plate 40. Here the embroidress has attempted to disguise the repeats by working the leaves in each unit with different filler patterns.

Most of the late 17th and early 18th century crewelwork branches are thick with foliage, and greens predominate in the colour scheme with only here and there a flower. This taste may hark back to verdure tapestries. Tapestries were the ultimate in wall hangings but beyond the means of most people and either embroideries or painted canvas had long served as a substitute. Perhaps, in some instances, crewelwork bedcurtains were also a complement to a bedroom hung with tapestry. Tastes changed in the 18th century and the heavy baroque style gave way to gay, flowering branches, rich in colour, and highly stylized leaf forms were discarded for more natural kinds. It is now often possible to recognise familiar garden favourites. In Plate 45 lilies, peonies, roses and columbine are among those depicted.

There were also technical changes. Many different stitches were employed in earlier crewelwork but in later examples chain stitch often predominates. The source of this change comes from India. Large quantities of embroideries from Gujerat, worked entirely in chain stitch with silk on fine cotton twill, were being imported into Europe from the 17th century on. As in the case of Indian painted cottons, called chintzes, it was the technique rather than the designs which inspired Western craftsmen. Chain stitch had long been part of the English embroidress's repertoire but now, as illustrated in many 18th century crewelwork curtains, it was often used to the exclusion of almost all other stitches. Some silk embroideries of the period are also worked almost entirely in chain stitch but they are on a smaller scale and it is much easier to give the impression of even lines of stitching with wool than with silk, since it is more inclined to spread.

Not all pieces classified as crewelwork are worked on a linen and cotton twill. Other materials were used when considered more suitable to the purpose. The set of curtains, Plate 41, is on a weft satin linen, the cord-quilted chainstitch coverlet, Plate 47, is on a linen tabby, the gown, Plate 50, also worked mostly chainstitch, is on Indian cotton 2/2 twill, and the kind used for Indian silk chainstitch embroidery. Nor is the branching style limited to crewelwork. The silk dress, Plate 67, has a repeating branch design which, though worked with silks, is stylistically related to crewelwork.

---

[1] See Patricia Wardle *Guide to English Embroidery,* Victoria and Albert Museum, 1970, cat. no. 46. Also Margaret H. Swain *Historical Needlework*, London, 1970, plate 13. This shows a crewelwork fragment on linen and cotton twill stamped "1640 Bruges."
[2] *Ibid.*
[3] A set of wallhangings and chair covers of point de Venise lace, mounted on blue

cloth, has a design of large branches in
the crewelwork style; they were formerly
at Kimberley House, Norfolk, and are
now in the C. L. David Collection,
Copenhagen. See *Apollo* vol. XVI, no. 94,
p. 162 and Gudmund Boesen *Danish
Museums*, Copenhagen, 1966.

38. Part of a Set of Curtains
17th century, second half
Acc. no. 971.228.1 a-c. Neg.no.71MISCTEX7
Repeat L. 86.5 cm, W. 106.5 cm

     Linen warp and cotton weft in 2/1
twill embroidered with 2-ply worsted yarns,
in shades of green, in encroaching satin,
stem, coral and back stitches.
     The design is a repeating one of
large fanciful leaves on sturdy curving
stems. The "seaweed" filler patterns are
light and airy compared with the heavily
worked outlines. The largest leaves measure
about fourteen inches in length. There is
piecing, and border scraps which may be
parts of valances. One is worked on a
chevron twill. The set came from Melchett
Hall.

39. Pair of Curtains. 1696
Acc. no. 961.120.1 and 961.178. Neg. no.
61AA1035
.120.1: L. 182.8 cm, W. 106.7 cm
.178: L. 179 cm, W. 88.2 cm

Linen warp, cotton weft in 2/1 twill
embroidered with firmly plyed 3-ply
worsted yarn, mostly in shades of green
and brown, in stem, satin, long and short,
coral, back stitch, Florentine, brick,
running, Vandyke, Cretan, tied herringbone,
chain, French knot, spaced buttonhole
fillings, bullion, Algerian eye, detached
chain, Roumanian, double back stitches,
laid and couched work.

The design is of treelets with large
fanciful leaves and slender flower and leaf
sprays growing from small grassy mounds.
Birds perch on some of the leaves. A repeat
of the designs begins near the top. 161.120.1
has the date 1696 embroidered on the trunk
of one of the treelets and a monogram
above. Neither of the curtains is complete
at any of the edges.(¹) The large number of
different stitches employed is unusual.
Published:
K. B. Brett. English Crewelwork Curtains in
the Royal Ontario Museum. *Embroidery,*
Volume 16, no. 1, Spring 1965, pp. 13-15.

(¹) There is another curtain from the set in
Victoria and Albert Museum, acc. no.
T166.1961, and a fourth piece in a
private American collection. An old
photograph in the Textile Department of
the Victoria and Albert Museum shows a
matching valance. Its present
whereabouts is unknown.

Detail of curtain, page 45.

40. Bed Curtain

Late 17th or early 18th century
Acc. no. 959.60.2. Neg. no. 101W59
L. 203.1 cm, W. 163.8 cm, S-S 48.9 cm

Linen warp, cotton weft in chevron twill embroidered with 2- and 3-ply worsted yarns, mostly in shades of green and brown, in long and short, fishbone, stem, French knot, running, back, chain, plaited edge stitches, laid and couched work.

A large curving branch growing from a low hillock repeats both vertically and horizontally. The foliage is mixed and there are sprays of small flowers; birds and squirrels perch on the foliage.

This is a splendid example of a repeated pattern in branching crewel work. The embroidress has helped to disguise the repeat by varying the filler patterns in each unit.

Published:
K. B. Brett. Crewelwork curtains in the Royal Ontario Museum, *Embroidery,* Volume 16, no. 1, Spring 1965, pp. 13-15

41. Set of Curtains
Late 17th or early 18th century
Acc. no. 971.227. a-d. Neg. no. 71TEX108
Wide curtains: L. 197 cm, W. 234 cm
Narrow curtains: L. 197 cm, W. 131 cm

Linen weft satin embroidered with coloured 2-ply wools in split, long and short, stem, French knot, and satin stitches, laid and couched work.

Each of the wide curtains has three flowering trees[1] growing from low mounds and the narrow pair has a single tree. All have fanciful leaves and many red flowers. The trees on both are the same but there are variations in embroidery stitches and secondary flowers and foliage. The side edges appear to be incomplete on some pieces, the filler patterns in several leaves having been worked but not the areas of solid embroidery. All the solid areas except those in French knot are worked on both sides, often in split stitch to give added firmness to the embroidery. The embroidery is worked through two layers of linen, the under one being loosely woven linen tabby. There is much use of French knots, sometimes for entire flowers and leaves, and the embroidery throughout is exceptionally fine.

---

[1] Only two trees and part of the third now remain. Total width approximately 335 cm.

48

42. Pair of Bed Curtains
Late 17th to early 18th century
Acc. no. 914X37 a & b. Neg. no. 66TEX90
L. 184.1 cm, W. 109.2 cm

Linen warp, cotton weft. 2/1 twill embroidered with coloured 2-ply worsted yarn, mostly double, in chain, long and short stitches, and French knots.

Heavy sprays of flowers and foliage almost entirely fill the space above a row of high hillocks across the bottom of the curtains. Among them are closely massed leafy plants growing from small mounds. The motifs and their positions are the same on each curtain but there are variations in stitches and the angles at which they are placed. They are worked mostly in long and short stitches, but split stitch occurs frequently because the yarn is double and when working long and short stitch the needle has been inserted through the cloth between the two yarns. Green is the predominant colour. The curtains have recently been remounted since the ground was badly worn.

49

43. Part of Curtain
Early 18th century
Acc. no. 916.13.2. Neg. no. 61K37 58
L. 130.8 cm, W. 132 cm, S-S 44.5 cm

Linen warp, cotton weft in 2/1 twill embroidered with 2-ply worsted yarn in shades of red in stem, buttonhole, long and short, chain, coral, French knot, detached chain, double back, and running stitches.

A serpentine branch with mixed flowers and foliage runs down each side and across the bottom. In the centre are staggered rows of small flowering plants including rose, carnation, lily and morning glory. Many of the flowers and leaves in the design are patterned with fancy fillings. The curtain has been cut off at the top. It is made of three lengths of twill joined before embroidering.

Another piece from the same set is in the Victoria and Albert Museum. It has been repaired with part of a third curtain.

44. Set of Bed Hangings

18th century, first quarter
Acc. no. 958.21.1 a–j. Neg. no. 19W59,
21W59
Wide curtains .a, .b: L. 210 cm, W. 218 cm
Narrow curtains .c, .d: L. 210 cm, W. 124 cm
Valances .e, .f: L. 177 cm, W. 28 cm
.g: L. 137 cm, W. 28 cm
Bases .h, .j: L. 178 cm, W. 29 cm
.i: L. 91 cm, W. 30 cm
S–S 89.5 cm

Linen warp, cotton weft 2/1 twill
embroidered with coloured 2-ply yarn in
chain and Roumanian, buttonhole, French
knot, running, stem, satin, double cross,
bullion, back, double back, satin, long and
short and coral, and detached chain stitches
and laid and couched work.

Tall, and somewhat angular, holly
branches grow from low grassy hillocks and
extend the length of the curtain in a slightly
diagonal movement. The designs on
valances and bases are small repeated
treelets. Most of the embroidery is in
chainstitch. The fabric is uniform except
parts of two valances (or bases) which are
worked on a fancy twill with linen warp
and cotton weft and it is mostly in these
that many different stitches besides
chain occur.

The work seems to have been done
by several hands. In some parts the foliage
is thicker than in others and some have
more filler patterns than others.
Published:
K. B. Brett, Crewelwork Curtains in the
Royal Ontario Museum, *Embroidery,* Volume
16, no. 1, Spring 1965, pp. 13-15.

45. Bedcurtain

18th century, second quarter
Acc. no. 972.12. Neg. no. 68MISCTEX159
Gift of Mrs. Edgar J. Stone
L. 225.4 cm, W. 218.4 cm, S-S 43.8 cm

Linen warp and cotton weft in 2/1 twill embroidered with coloured 2-ply wools mostly in chain stitch and a few French knots.

The curtain is composed of five widths of twill which were stitched together before embroidering began. Two units of the design, of large meandering branches bearing many miscellaneous flowers, almost fill the entire curtain except at the side edges where there are partial repeats.

The curtain must have been one of a set of four. Sets usually comprised two narrow curtains for the head of the bed and two wide ones to go around the foot and partway along each side. The organization of the design in this one suggests that the curtains matched and repeating branches appeared continuous around the bed when drawn.

52

46. Curtain

18th century, second half
Acc. no. 945.8.9. Neg. no. 62AA220
Repeat L. 54.6 cm, W. 44.4 cm to 96.5 cm

    White linen tabby embroidered with coloured 2-ply worsted yarn in stem, chain, Roumanian, bullion, satin, double back, cross, French knot, buttonhole, and long and short stitches.

    The design repeats a branch meander with small mixed flowers and foliage. The design has been inspired by or copied from an Indian painted cotton or an English copperplate printed cotton of the third quarter of the century. The curtain is considerably pieced and has probably been made up from parts of a set of curtains. The lightweight linen and slender branches are in strong contrast to the sturdy crewelwork curtains of the earlier part of the century.

53

47. Coverlet

Early 18th century
Acc. no. 949.189. Neg. no. C65A51 and
71TEX86 (detail showing quilting)
Gift of Mrs. Edgar J. Stone.
L. 205.6 cm, W. 167.6 cm

White linen tabby embroidered
with coloured 2-ply worsted yarns in chain,
detached chain, stem, satin, buttonhole,
French knot, and speckling stitches, and
laid and couched work.

The same flowering plants with
large flowers growing from a tiny mound
repeats with variations in each corner and
the central medallion is composed of four
other variants. They are worked on two
widths of linen, mostly in chain stitch. One
flower, in a corner plant, has the initials PL
in the centre. The elaborate floral and
scrolling ground is cord quilted in running
stitch. The under layer is a light brown
linen tabby with paired wefts and the
quilting cords are soft 3- and 4-ply cotton.

The central medallion is worked
nearer one end than the other which is an
unusual feature.

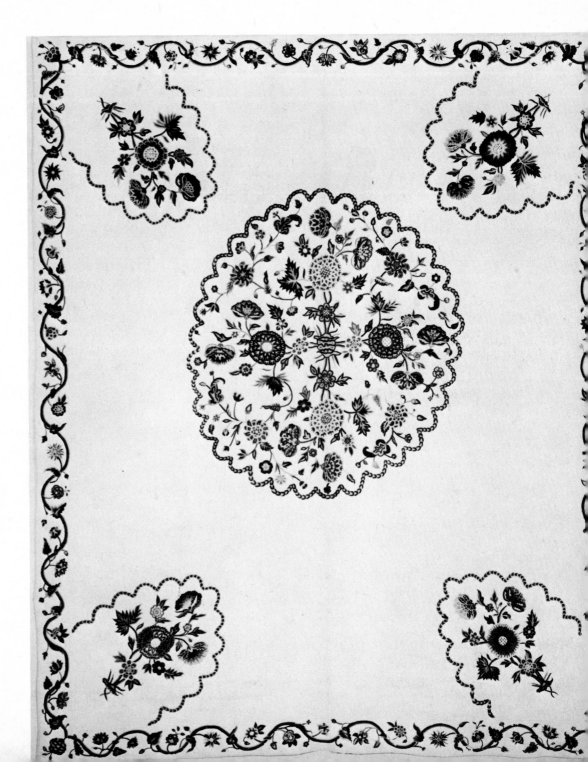

54

Detail of coverlet, page 54.

48. Coverlet. 1728
Acc. no. 970.128. Neg. no. 70MISCTEX10
Gift of Mr. and Mrs. Edgar J. Stone in
memory of Gerard Brett
L. 130.8 cm, W. 139 cm

Linen warp and cotton weft 2/1
twill embroidered with coloured 2-ply
worsted yarns in chain, buttonhole, stem,
French knot and hollie stitches.

The ground is filled with small
flowering plants, birds, animals and
Chinoiserie figures. Two flying angels at
the top, in the centre, hold a shield bearing
the date 1728 and the initials E.L., and at
the bottom there is a reclining figure in a
bed beneath a canopy. The border of
inverted scallops has a flower spray in each
scallop and a heart-shaped motif in each
corner.

The coverlet is composed of three
widths of twill. The pattern does not match
at the join on the right.

49. Valance

18th century, first half
Acc. no. 916.13.1. Neg. no. 62AA218
L. 147.3 cm, W. 27.9 cm

Linen warp, cotton weft, 2/1 twill embroidered with coloured 2-ply worsted yarns in satin, encroaching surface satin, French knots, chain, cross, and double cross stitches.

A large red bird, resembling a peacock with outspread wings, is perched on a chevron-patterned serpentine branch in the centre of the valance. The branch bears three composite leaf-flowers and simple leaf forms. Part of the design has been cut off at the left side. It is worked almost entirely in satin stitches.

50. Gown

18th century, first half
Acc. no. 934.4.423. Neg. no. 63AA172-177
(details)
The Harry Wearne Collection. Gift of
Mrs. Harry Wearne
L. 158 cm, S-S 108 cm

White 2/2 glazed cotton twill
embroidered with coloured 2-ply wools
mostly in chain, buttonhole, detached
chain stitches, and some French knots.

The scattered array of flora and
fauna have been drawn from several
sources. In the centre of the back is a scene
from Aesop's fable The Fox and the Grapes.
The ox and the frog, and other groups such
as a cat and a rat may also be from fables.
Some of the flower sprays, such as borage
and heartsease, are so carefully drawn as
to suggest a botanical source. Other more
fanciful flowers were probably from pattern
books. Some of the birds and insects are
recognisable and may be from bestiaries.
The gown is no longer made up and the
sleeves have been removed. The pieces were
cut out and embroidered before sewing. By
extending the branches of the flower at the
top of the back allowance has been made
for pleats.

Chair seat cover embroidered
on linen canvas; 18th century, first
half. The cover was never
blocked or cut from the canvas.
See page 62.

Eighteenth Century Canvas Work

Eighteenth century canvas work has had a long lasting effect on English embroidery right through the 19th century and down to the present day. It was worked, like its descendants, on linen canvas with coloured wools and silks in cross and tent stitch, today called petit point, gros point, or by the misnomer of "tapestry work." Many of the finest 18th century examples are to be found on upholstery for chairs, stools, and settees and were often the triumph of the amateur embroidress, her family, and her friends. Mrs. Delany has several comments in her letters about assisting the Duchess of Portland with chair seats. At one point a set they were working on got dropped and was only picked up and completed fourteen years later. Many ambitious projects, such as coverings for the furnishings of an entire room, may well have taken years to complete, depending, of course, on how many were working on it and the diligence of the embroidresses. No doubt the time element partly accounts for an almost classic style in many embroideries for chairs in the first half of the 18th century. A favourite was that with either one or two figures in a landscape setting surrounded by a rich floral border and sometimes within a cartouche. Other figure subjects were chosen from biblical stories or classical mythology and were probably inspired by similar designs on tapestry upholstery which only the rich could afford. Another subject with many variations was a vase, a basket, or a bouquet of mixed flowers either with or without a border. Borders tended to be narrower in the second quarter of the century than in the first.

More ambitious undertakings in canvas work were hangings and floor carpets. Understandably these were highly prized possessions since, although in the case of carpets they were more coarsely worked than upholstery, they represented a vast amount of work and presumably presented problems when embroidered in one piece, that is after the lengths of canvas had been stitched together. Carpets were part of the professionals' repertoire and many that have survived must have been professionally embroidered.

Many small pieces such as cushion covers, pole, and hand screens, purses and other accessories belong to this group. Pictures also come into this category but they are discussed in another section. Some, such as Plate 29, were originally set into looking glass frames, in a panel below the glass.

51. Pair of Chair Seat Covers

18th century, first half
Acc. no. 969.323.2 a and b
Neg. no. 68MISCTEX65 and 66
Gift of Mrs. Edgar J. Stone
L. 58.4 cm, W. 68.6 cm

Linen canvas embroidered with coloured 2-ply worsted yarns and silks in tent stitch.

On each cover a woman is depicted seated beneath a tree in a landscape setting and conversing with a man who stands before her. In 969.323.2a the woman wears a broad-brimmed hat and the man holds a cane; in 969.323.2b Harlequin hands a shepherdess a note. The covers have matching floral borders and have never been blocked or cut from the canvas which has selvages at the edges.

The pair is part of a set of six, all with a man and woman in a landscape setting and with the same border.

52. Chair Seat Cover
18th century, second quarter
Acc. no. 967.51. Neg. no. 71TEX94
L. 56.5 cm, W. 56 cm

Linen canvas embroidered with coloured 2-ply wool doubled and silk floss in tent and cross stitches.

A large central cartouche encloses two figures on a grassy mound beneath a tree. A man stands playing a bagpipe and a woman sits listening with a spotted dog beside her. This area is worked entirely in tent stitch. The surround of flowers and foliage, much of which has been cut away, is worked in coarser cross stitch with groups of three and four 2-ply strands of yarn.

53. Chair
Early 18th century
Acc. no. 968.26.1
Gift of The W. Garfield Weston Charitable Foundation
Back panel of embroidery H. 87 cm, W. 54 cm

Linen canvas ground embroidered with 2-ply wools in tent stitch with accents in satin stitch.

The subject is the sacrifice of Isaac in a landscape setting within a scroll cartouche. Isaac kneels on a low stone block with Abraham bending over him with sword upraised. A restraining angel hovers above grasping the sword blade with one hand. A small elephant peers out of the shrubbery at the left. The cartouche is set on a white semé ground which the top of the seat cushion matches.

54. Pole Screen
18th century, first half
Acc. no. 970.187.A
L. 65.5 cm, W. 58.1 cm

    Linen canvas embroidered with coloured wools and pale yellow silk in cross and tent stitch.
    The scene depicted is Jacob's Dream. Jacob reclines under a tree in the lower left corner and the upper part of the picture is filled with angels ascending a large ladder into a mass of clouds from which a rayed sun shines forth. The picture has a border of large flowers and leaves typical of the period.

55. Carpet
About 1740
Acc. no. 968.238. Neg. no. 71MISC TEX 3
Gift of The W. Garfield Weston Charitable Foundation
L. 409 cm, W. 274 cm

    Linen canvas embroidered with coloured 4-ply wools in tent stitch.
    There is a large flower spray in the centre surrounded by rococo scrolls. The border is of foliage scrolls, garlands and strapwork terminating with a foliate pedestal motif in each corner and a shell motif in the centre of each end. The entire carpet has a red and brown ground pattern of triangles, their points touching. The embroidery has been worked after the lengths of canvas have been joined together and the carpet is probably the work of a professional.

56. **Carpet**

Mid 18th century
L956.37. Neg. no. 61AA1036
Lent by Mrs. G. W. Robinette

Linen canvas embroidered with
4-ply coloured wools in cross and tent stitch.
The design is dominated by four
pointed corner medallions and an oval
floral medallion in the centre, which has a
bird within a lozenge in the middle. The
closely patterned flower and foliage ground,
interspersed with quatrefoils, repeats, but
numerous adjustments have been made to
work it in around the medallions. The
medallion border has intervening spaces
filled with foliage and on each side of
the corner motifs there are small lions
worked in tent stitch. The carpet has been
embroidered in one piece and could have
been an ambitious project by an inexper-
ienced embroidress who got a little confused
with the repeats in the field.

Elaborate floral border worked in silks on a man's waistcoat; 18th century, second quarter or a little later. See page 80.

Eighteenth Century
Silk Embroideries

Silk embroideries of the 18th century, with their glowing colours and general air of luxury, include many of the finest examples of English embroidery of the period. They fall into several groups: there are those worked by amateurs and those worked by professionals, those worked on silk and those on linen.

Their styles reflect other forms of English decoration and, as in them, flowers are the recurring theme. The greatest possible naturalism was the ideal in the 18th century and this, combined with precision of workmanship, often marks the line between the amateur and the professional. Chinoiserie, often inspired by Chinese embroideries rather than English creations in this style, also has its place in embroideries of the first half of the century as well as formal scroll work. The exquisite use of satin stitch in China and the skilled handling of chain stitch in Gujarat, India, were sources of inspiration in the use of these stitches.

The silks used range from floss to tightly twisted two-ply silks. A number of the embroideries are enriched with metal threads, silver and silver gilt filé, frisé and purl and also spangles.

By the beginning of the 18th century embroidery for costume had returned to favour after a lapse of half a century. The best represented articles in the Museum's collection are short aprons of the first half of the century. Often worked in the home, they were intended for decorative purposes only. Gowns, petticoats, and other garments and accessories were also embroidered and there are numerous references to these in contemporary diaries and letters,

particularly in the letters of Mrs. Delany, herself a skilled embroidress. The most striking example she gives us is a gown she saw in 1741 at Norfolk House which had been rented by Frederick, Prince of Wales. She relates in a letter to her sister that "The Duchess of Queensbury's clothes pleased me best; they were white satin embroidered, the bottom of the petticoat *brown hills* covered with all sorts of weeds, and *every breadth* had *an old stump of a tree* that run up almost to the top of the petticoat, broken and ragged and worked with brown chenille, and round which twined nasturtiums, ivy, honeysuckles, periwinkles, convolvuluses, and all sorts of twining flowers which spread and covered the petticoat, vines with leaves variegated as you have seen them by the sun, all rather smaller than nature, which made them look very light: the robings and facings were little green banks with all sorts of weeds, and the sleeves and the rest of the gown loose twining branches of the same sort as those on the petticoat: many of the leaves were finished with gold, and part of the stumps of the trees looked like the gilding of the sun. I never saw a piece of work so prettily fancied . . ." This gorgeous court costume would of course be the achievement of professional embroidresses; a court costume in the Victoria and Albert Museum is similarly worked. A modestly embroidered dress, Plate 67, is embroidered with a flowering branch on each breadth rather in the style of crewelwork.

Men's waistcoats were another costume item where embroidery played an important part. Many of these were

also the work of professionals. Sleeveless ones which came in the first quarter of the century had only the fronts and pocket flaps embroidered in a length of the silk which, when purchased, would be taken to a tailor to be made up.

Silk embroidered bed furniture on silk or linen was often the work of professionals. Among the most sumptuous were sets comprising a coverlet and matching cushions, in several sizes, worked on white satin with coloured silks and metal threads. The coverlet in Plate 72 superbly worked in silk only, and mostly in satin stitches, was probably part of such a set. Many of the flowers in the baskets and cornucopias can be identified, the bearded iris being the most remarkable piece of realism. Such embroideries were for display only. They were brought out on state occasions and only the wealthy could afford them.

Another group of late 17th and early 18th silk embroideries were worked with yellow silk on linen, mostly in back stitch. Here again is Indian influence, this time the tussar silk (naturally yellow) Indian embroideries from Bengal and worked on cotton. Back stitch, as noted in the section on crewelwork regarding chain stitch, had long been employed by English embroidresses but never as the predominating stitch as it often was in Bengali embroideries. Little inspiration for design came from India but the combination of yellow and white was an innovation. This type of embroidery was worked both for housefurnishings and for costume. The curtain in Plate 73 is the remains of a set of bed furniture and the petticoat, Plate 75, is an outstanding example of backstitch embroidery. It is possible that the English embroidresses' passion for fine ground patterns, suggesting quilting and worked in back stitch, was also Indian inspired, but since the embroideries were worked through two layers of fabric some such device was desirable to hold both layers together. An embroidery frame was also essential to keep the two layers in position.

57. Coverlet
18th century, first quarter
Acc. no. 923.4.56. Neg. no. 71TEX65
L. 144.8 cm, W. 171.4 cm

White satin embroidered with coloured 2-ply silks and silver gilt filé in satin, long and short, geometrical satin, French knot and stem stitches, and laid and couched work.

There is a basket of mixed flowers in the centre and in each corner, and three cornucopias of flowers along the sides. Sprays of small flowers trail from the bouquets to beneath the baskets and link them with the cornucopias. The entire ground is latticed with couched silver gilt filé, three strands being twisted together. Metal threads occur nowhere else. The flowers and foliage are worked naturalistically mostly in satin stitches and a number are recognisable such as iris, rose, tulip, anemone, holly, lily, and dianthus. The embroidery is worked through two layers of fabric, the under one being linen tabby. It is carefully organised so that flower and leaf sprays run along the two seams, concealing the join of the widths of satin.

The coverlet is related both stylistically and technically to two magnificent sets in the Victoria and Albert Museum[1].

---

[1] See Patricia Wardle. *A Guide to English Embroidery*, Plate 59.

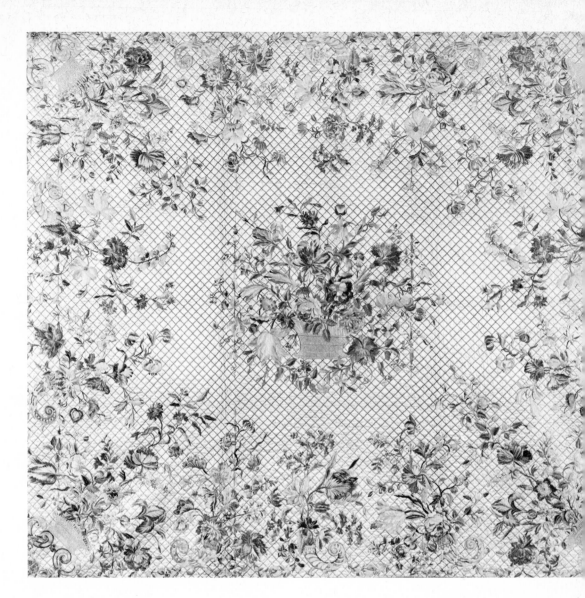

58. Panel
Late 17th or early 18th century
Acc. no. 961.120.2. Neg. no. 70TEX116
L. 132.1 cm, W. 147.3 cm

    Fine white linen tabby embroidered
with crimson, light brown and pale
yellow silks in back, buttonhole, stem,
satin, chain, coral and French knot stitches.
    In the centre and each corner
there is a symmetrical medallion
arrangement of slender scrolling stems
and foliage. The rest of the panel is filled
with rows of chinoiserie plants, many
growing from low mounds. There are
several depicting the lotus and some may
have been drawn directly from Chinese
sources, perhaps embroideries, painted
silks, or wallpaper. The ground is
embroidered with a small lattice in back
stitch. All the motifs are embroidered with
crimson silks. Details are picked out in
light brown and the lattice ground is pale
yellow. The embroidery has been worked
through two layers of fabric, the under one
a coarse cotton.

59. **Panel**
Late 17th to early 18th century
Acc. no. 911.2.6. Neg. no. ROMA 86.55
Chick Collection. Gift of Mrs. H. D. Warren
L. 33.6 cm, W. 27.6 cm

    White tabby silk embroidered
with coloured silks, silver, and silver gilt
filé and frisé wound over a white silk core,
silver purl, and cords of coloured silk and
silk frisé twisted together, in long and
short, stem, satin and split stitches, and laid
and couched work.
    A ewer worked with metallic threads
contains a mixed bouquet of flowers which
includes a rose, lily, columbine, tulip,
daffodil, carnation and hyacinth. The panel
may originally have been mounted in a
screen.

68

60. Cushion Cover
Early 18th century
Acc. no. 970.86. Neg. no. 71TEX89
Gift of Mr. G. W. Ralph
L. 58.1 cm, W. 40.7 cm

    White linen tabby embroidered
with coloured 2-ply silks and silver filé
and frisé wound on a pale yellow silk core,
in satin, long and short, and back stitches,
laid and couched work.
    A floral meander border terminates
in each corner and at the centre of each
side with a motif of stylized vases of foliage.
The central field is filled with a vermicelli
pattern worked in backstitch with yellow
silk. It is embroidered through two layers of
linen, and is backed with 17th century
Chinese, lotus-patterned, silk damask. The
edges are bound with silver filé tape.

61. **Cushion Cover**
Early 18th century
Acc. no. 927.42.3. Neg. no. 71TEX87
L. 71.1 cm, W. 45.1 cm

White linen tabby embroidered with
coloured floss silks in surface satin, long
and short, French knots, stem, and back
stitches, laid and couched work.

In the centre there is a large
flowerhead, with long pointed leaves around
it, which join in pairs at the tips and form
a six-pointed star. A related arrangement
fills each corner. Flowering branches stem
from the central motif across a ground
pattern of overlapping circles worked with
yellow silk in back stitch. The embroidery
is worked through two layers of linen, the
one at the back being very coarse.

The cushion cover has an irregular
horizontal join and has been made up from
two matching covers.

62. Short Apron
18th century, first half
Acc. no. 920.36.2. Neg. no. 71TEX18
L. 43.8 cm, W. 104.2 cm

White silk tabby, with slight rib,
embroidered with coloured 2-ply silk and
silver gilt filé, on a pale yellow silk core,
in long and short, bullion, satin, cross, and
stem stitches, and laid and couched work.

The central symmetrical flower and
foliage motif is flanked on either side by a
large spray of fanciful flowers and leaves
which stem from each lower corner and are
reversed mirrorwise. The sides and bottom
have narrow hems and the top has a wide
one through which a ribbon is run.

Some of the flowers and foliage may
have been inspired by those on Indian
painted cottons for the European market;
others may derive from 17th century Italian
embroideries.

71

63. Short Apron
18th century, first half
Acc. no. 920.36.1. Neg. no. 71TEX24
L. 45 cm, W. 102.9 cm

White silk tabby with slight rib, embroidered with 2-ply coloured silks in two weights, silver gilt filé and frisé on yellow silk cores, silver frisé on a white silk core and green silk filé wound round a linen core in satin, chain, stem, speckling, French knot, long and short, double cross and cross stitches, and laid and couched work.

Three flowering branches extend from bottom to top, those on either side of the centre being identical but one is reversed mirrorwise. A smaller branch trails up the edge at each side. The branches are joined together at the bottom by curving stems terminating in large leaves worked with lattice and cross stitch filler patterns. All bear mixed flowers and foliage. The apron is pleated into a narrow waistband and the bottom edge is scalloped. The finer two-ply silk is used for couching the filé and frisé threads.

64. Short Apron
18th century, first half
Acc. no. 926.31. Neg. no. 71TEX31
L. 42.6 cm, W. 101.6 cm

White silk tabby, with slight rib,
embroidered with coloured 2-ply silks,
silver gilt purl, silver and silver gilt filé
and frisé wound on an ivory silk core in
satin, long and short, French knot stitches,
and laid and couched work.

Baskets in the centre and at an angle
in each corner hold a plant bearing tulips,
grapes, strawberries, pears and wheat. A
small mixed bouquet in a jar on either
side of the centre basket has a bird
perched on the top of it. There are various
filler patterns. Around the bottom there is
an inset of silver gilt filé mesh.

All the embroidery, except tendrils
and some stems, has been applied to the
apron, and since it is worked on a similar
silk it may have been cut from
another apron.

65. Short Apron
18th century, first half
Acc. no. 925.43.2. Neg. no. 71TEX25
L. 49.5 cm, W. 102.9 cm

White silk tabby, with slight rib,
embroidered with 2-ply coloured silks,
silk filé over a linen thread in long and
short, stem, French knot, cross, double
cross stitches, couching and sheaf fillings.

A small flowering plant in the centre
is flanked by two taller plants on either
side. Those on one side are reversed
mirrorwise to those on the other. All have
mixed flowers and foliage and are linked
across the bottom by a trailing branch that
stems from the plant at each end. There is a
simple selvage across the top. The sides
and bottom are hemmed. There are various
combinations used for filler patterns such
as double cross and sheaf fillings.

A worn ridge across the top
indicates where the top edge was once
turned down. It probably had a ribbon
run through it.

74

66. Short Apron
18th century, first half
Acc. no. 925.43.3. Neg. no. 71TEX18
L. 50.2 cm, W. 109.2 cm

White silk tabby with slight rib embroidered with 2-ply coloured silks and green silk filé wound around a linen core, in buttonhole, stem, long and short, and herringbone stitches and couching.

Identical flowering branches, one reversed mirrorwise, stem from the lower corners of the apron, and a flowering plant in the centre has branches which spread, encircle a flower, and almost join above it. There are various filler patterns. The sides and bottom have wide shallow scallops finished with buttonholing. There is a worn ridge and stitch holes below the selvage edge at the top, indicating a turn down for a drawstring.

67. Dress. 1730s-1740s
Acc. no. 925.43.1. Neg. no. ROMA2052

    White silk tabby, with slight rib, embroidered with coloured 2-ply silks in long and short, French knot, stem, satin and herring bone stitches.

    Each of the five widths of silk, which compose the skirt, has the same flowering branch meander with minor variations in the mixed flowers and foliage. The branch ends at the top of the skirt but is cut off at the bottom. Pieces from other widths with the same pattern have been used for the bodice. There are various filler patterns.

    The branch design is stylistically similar to those in some crewel work curtains of the first half of the 18th century. The dress is cut with the back *en fourreau* and wide cuffed sleeves. Folded robings extend to the waist.

76

68. Embroidered Petticoat
18th century, second quarter
Acc. no. 932.23. Neg. no. 71TEX88
L. 94 cm, Circ. 365.6 cm

Coral pink satin embroidered with white 2-ply silk in satin, stem, running, French knots, cross and double cross stitches, in various filler patterns, and raised laid and couched work.

The pattern runs around the lower part of the skirt and is composed of three alternating flowering plants with mixed flowers and foliage. There are various filler patterns. The petticoat is lined with glazed wool tabby, padded with wool, and held with lattice quilting in running stitch.

There is considerable piecing which suggests that the petticoat may have been made from the skirt of an embroidered dress. The lining and quilting are contemporary and the quilting was done after piecing. It is said to be a wedding petticoat of 1747.

69. Stomacher
18th century, first half
Acc. no. 922.28.11. Neg. no. 71TEX58
L. 30.5 cm (not including tabs)

White linen tabby embroidered with
coloured 2-ply silks and silver filé in satin,
long and short, French knot, and stem
stitches, and laid and couched work.

The triangular shape is filled with
a flowering plant, which has a large
carnation near the top. Other flowers
branching from it have scrolling tendrils.
A narrow band, embroidered with a
meander pattern and eyelet holes, is bound
with yellow satin ribbon and stitched to each
side of the stomacher. A cord of silver filé
is laced across. There are four small ribbon
tabs at intervals down each side edge and
four embroidered ones stitched to the
rounded point at the bottom.

Embroidered stomachers, which
filled in the front of the bodice of a dress,
often gave a note of contrast or matching
colour to the costume.

78

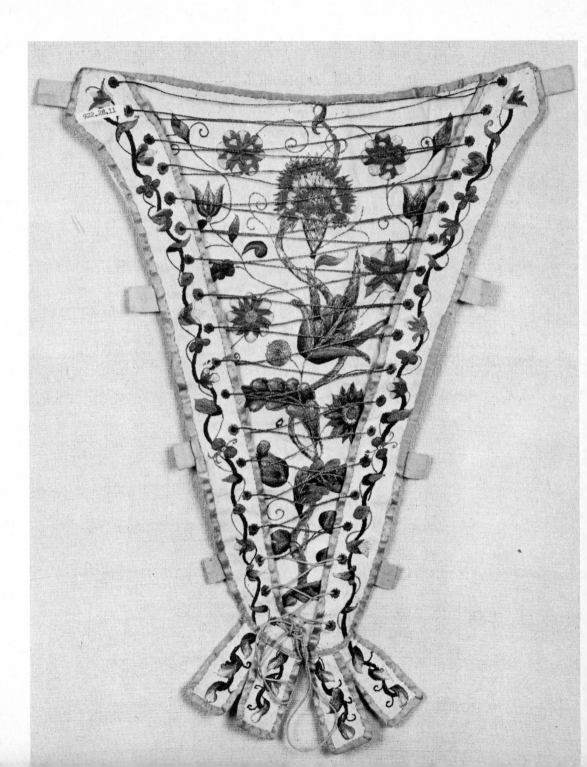

70. Man's Sleeved Waistcoat
Early 18th century
Acc. no. 924.22. Neg. no. C191.52.
L. 90 cm

White tabby linen embroidered with coloured 2-ply silks in two weights and single and 2-ply silver gilt filé in chain, buttonhole, and back stitches, and couched and laid work.

The design of branch meanders, where large chinoiserie birds perch, extends down the fronts and around the skirts to the back vent. Related flowers are worked around the lower part of the sleeves and the entire linen surface, back and front, is worked with a small back stitch lattice. The plied coloured silks have a firm twist resembling those in 18th century Chinese embroideries for the European market. The yellow silk used for couching is finer and has a looser ply. The workmanship has the precision of a professional hand.

The waistcoat has been made from an embroidered coverlet probably worked in the late 17th century since the history of the waistcoat is that it belonged to the stepson of Admiral Sir Clowdisley Shovell who was lost with his stepfather off the Scilly Isles in 1707.

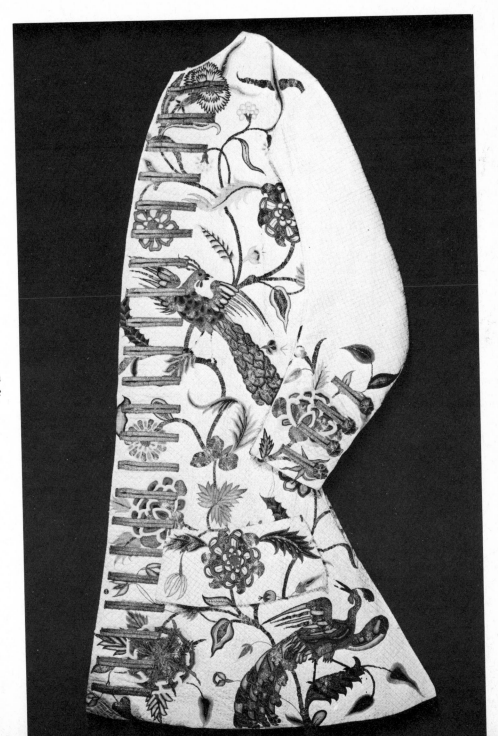

71. **Waistcoat**

18th century, second quarter or a little later
Acc. no. 912X14.4 a & b. Neg. no. 71TEX33
L. 94 cm

White satin worked with coloured
2-ply silks, silver gilt purl, silver gilt filé and
frisé over a white silk core in satin, long
and short, French knot, stem stitches and
laid and couched work, spangles.

An elaborate floral border covers
almost the entire surface. The design is well
organized to fit the shape of the garment
and to incorporate the pocket flap. The
joins of the flaps to the fronts are almost
entirely concealed by embroidery. The plied
silk yarn resembles that in Chinese
embroideries for export. The embroidery is
worked with great precision; some of the
couching has been done to suggest veining
in the leaves. The satin is backed with a
coarse linen and the embroidery worked
through both fabrics. There are thirteen
buttonholes on the left side extending to
the top of the pocket flap.

The style and richness of the
embroidery is similar to that on the coverlet
in Plate 57 and related pieces, and is the
work of a professional. The waistcoat has
been taken apart.

72. **Small Coverlet**

Early 18th century
Gift of Mrs. C. R. Cumberland
Acc. no. 949.27.5
L. 111.8 cm, W. 101.6 cm

White linen tabby embroidered
with yellow 2-ply silk in back and satin
stitches.

An allover lattice pattern is formed
by long narrow leaves, and there is a circular
spot at the intersections and in the centre of
each interstice. The embroidery is worked
through two layers of linen, that on the
back being rather coarse. The edges are
bound with yellow silk tape.

73. Panel
Early 18th century
Acc. no. 957.48. Neg. no. 62AA225
L. 243.1 cm, W. 218.4 cm

White tabby linen embroidered with yellow 2-ply silk in back, stem, buttonhole, and Cretan stitches.

The panel has an allover repeating symmetrical pattern of interlacing slender scrolls and palmettes. The embroidery is worked through two layers of linen, the under one rather coarse. The panel is considerably pieced since it is made up from what was once a set of bed curtains.

74. Cushion Cover
Early 18th century
Acc. no. 962.98. Neg. no. 62AA216
Gift of Miss Katherine Brichta
L. 52.5 cm, W. 66.5 cm

      White linen tabby embroidered with yellow 2-ply silk in back, double back and satin stitches.

      The design is a repeating one of narrow curving and interlacing bands and the spaces between are worked with diaper and other filler patterns. The embroidery is worked through two layers of linen, the one at the back being rather coarse. The embroidery terminates near the edge of the linen on all four sides but the pattern has not been planned to fit the shape it is worked on. This seems to have been intentional.

75. Parts of a Petticoat
Early 18th century
Acc. no. 948.251.3. Neg. no. 71 TEX 62
Gift of Miss Amice Calverley
Each part—L. 82 cm, W. 134 cm

White linen 2/2 twill. Warps and wefts in pairs. Embroidered with pale yellow silk in back stitch.

Two alternating vertical bands repeat around the skirt. Both have slender flower and foliage meanders, one on a lattice ground. There is a wider band with a similar pattern around the bottom and a line of back stitch along the top edge. It is worked through two layers of fabric, the one at the back being cotton tabby.

The petticoat has been cut in two pieces and joined along the top edge to make a coverlet. Two side edges match but the other sides are incomplete.

76. Pair of Mittens
Early 18th century
Acc. no. 961.145 a and b. Neg. no. 71TEX103
L. 35.8 cm

 White linen tabby embroidered with
yellow 2-ply silk in back stitch.
 An allover quatrefoil pattern is
worked through two layers of linen. On
the backs of the mittens are two trapezoidal
panels worked in a little scale pattern.
There is a horizontal slit on the inside
across the lower part of the fingers but the
opening to the upper part, which would
cover the fingers, has been stitched down.
The thumbs are open, the fabric coming to
a point over the nail. All edges are bound
with linen tape.

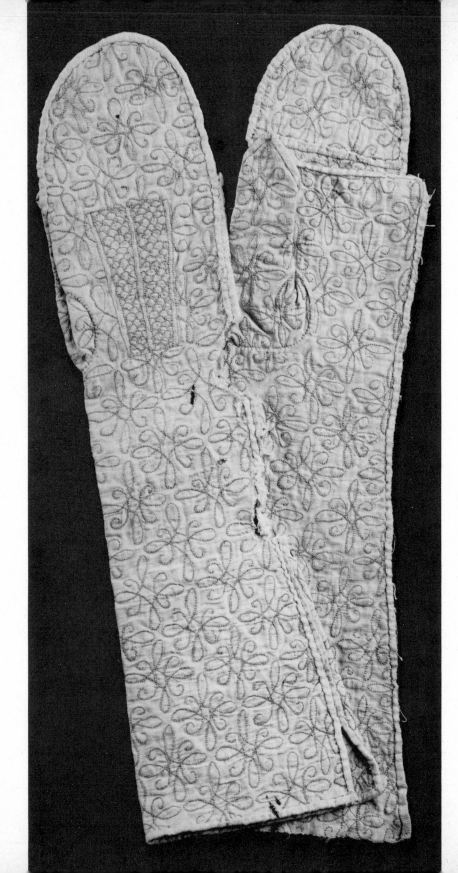

84

Detail of 1672 band sampler shows several border patterns and two alphabets. See page 16.

Quilting and Whitework

Decorative quilting of many kinds and for many purposes was done in England in the 18th century. The most elaborate and intricate was cord quilting, sometimes called Italian quilting. It was a particular favourite in the early part of the century and is done in double lines of back or running stitch through two layers of fabric, usually linen, following the curves of the design as required but leaving enough space between the lines to run short lengths of soft cord between the two layers. The bearing cloth in Plate 77 shows how complex this technique can be, especially if enhanced with drawn work, and the coverlet in Plate 78 is another example of an elaborate design worked in running stitch. This type of cord quilting was done in Europe as well as in the British Isles and the styles are almost indistinguishable.

Another decorative kind of quilting was done in running stitch on silk petticoats for winter wear. They were backed with wool tabby and padded with wool and worn instead of the matching petticoat of a gown. Many have survived to the present day and a number of these have been altered to fit under the full skirts of the mid 19th century. A deep border of flowers and scrolling foliage ran around the lower part of the skirt and served a practical as well as a decorative purpose in holding the padding in place. The upper part of the skirt was filled with lattice quilting. Bed curtains, valances and coverlets were often quilted in simple lattices in running stitch for both

firmness and warmth, to keep out draughts. Infants' garments were also quilted for warmth.

The North of England and South Wales were the two great centres of quilt making in the 18th and 19th century and each has its distinctive style. Many were made at home by the women of the household, a few hours every day being set aside for quilting. There were also itinerant quilters who went from house to house staying several weeks at each. Wedding quilts were the most elaborate, and the satin quilt in this collection, which was made into an elegant morning gown, may have been such a one.

Fine white embroidery on linen or muslin had many costume uses in the 18th century. Baby clothes are among the most exquisite examples of fine sewing and white needlework, particularly the "hollie" point fillings used for bonnet crowns and as openwork bands on the shoulders of shirts. Sleeve ruffles, kerchiefs and aprons of sheer muslin often had a combination of open and solid embroidery. The sleeve ruffle in Plate 79, for instance, has many different drawnwork patterns giving a light lacy effect in contrast to other parts worked with white cotton in close rows of darning stitch.

At the end of the 18th century, when white muslin was fashionable for dresses, dainty sprig and spot patterns were embroidered on it both by professionals and in the home. The late 18th century embroidered apron, Plate 80, is an example of the kind of sprigged pattern worked by skilled amateur needlewomen and which, on an even smaller scale, was fashionable for dresses at the end of the century.

77. Coverlet, called a Bearing Cloth Robe
Early 18th century
Acc. no. 953.93. Neg. no. 32.18a56
Gift of the Misses Ormsby
L. 102.9 cm; W. 92.7 cm

Fine white linen tabby embroidered with white linen in back and running stitches, French knots and various drawn work fillings.

The coverlet is worked solidly with cord quilting and fancy fillings, many of them in drawn work. A large floral medallion in the centre is surrounded by sprays of flowers and an elaborate floral border stems from each corner and terminates at a cartouche in the centre of each side. The edges are scalloped. The embroidery is worked through two layers of linen and a soft cotton cord has been used for padding.

The coverlet is said to be Irish by tradition but is identical in style and workmanship with English examples of this type of embroidery[1].

---

[1] One example may be seen in Patricia Wardle *Guide to English Embroidery,* Victoria and Albert Museum, plate 71.

78. Quilt
Probably Northumberland, 18th century
Acc. no. 942.9.1. Neg. no. 71TEX90
Gift of Mrs. H. Hopkirk

White satin backed with white silk
tabby and quilted with 2-ply white silk in
running stitch.

There is a large circular medallion
in the centre of the field and a matching
segment in each corner. The medallion has
a large square in the centre divided into
small squares each containing a flower
motif, and it also has a repeating spiral
border pattern. The ground is lattice quilted
with large pairs of feathery leaves poised
at the edges of the medallion and segments.
The wide border is divided into patterned
triangles and has wide guard borders of
repeated patterned ellipses. The quilt is
lightly padded and has been cut up and
made into a man's morning gown in an
18th century straight cut style.

79. Sleeve Ruffle

18th century, first quarter
Acc. no. 964.237.2. Neg. no. 71TEX37
Gift of Miss Katharine McLennan
L. 99.1 cm. Greatest Width 19.1 cm

White tabby muslin embroidered with white cotton in buttonhole and darning stitches and drawn work.

The design of flower and foliage sprays has slender stems, tenuous leaves, and large fanciful flowers. Each part of every flower is filled with one of more than fifteen filler patterns in drawn work.

An apron in the Victoria and Albert Museum is stylistically and technically similar and is dated 1717[1].

---

[1] See Patricia Wardle, *Guide to English Embroidery*, cat. no. 79.

80. Apron. 1790-1797
Acc. no. 933.46. Neg. no. 71TEX38
Gift of Mrs. F. B. Reid
L. 107.9 cm, W. 134.6 cm

Sheer white muslin embroidered with white cotton in satin, chain and buttonhole stitches and various drawnwork fillings.

Repeating flower sprays across the bottom form a border and above them are looped garlands held by ribbon bows. Each loop and also those of the bows are filled with small drawnwork diaper patterns. The rest of the apron is embroidered with alternating rows of flower sprigs and leaves. There is a scalloped picotted border down the sides and across the bottom. The embroidery is incomplete at the top where the edge is raw.

The apron was embroidered by Mrs. Edward Archer and her sister at Mildenhall, Suffolk, between 1790 and 1797.

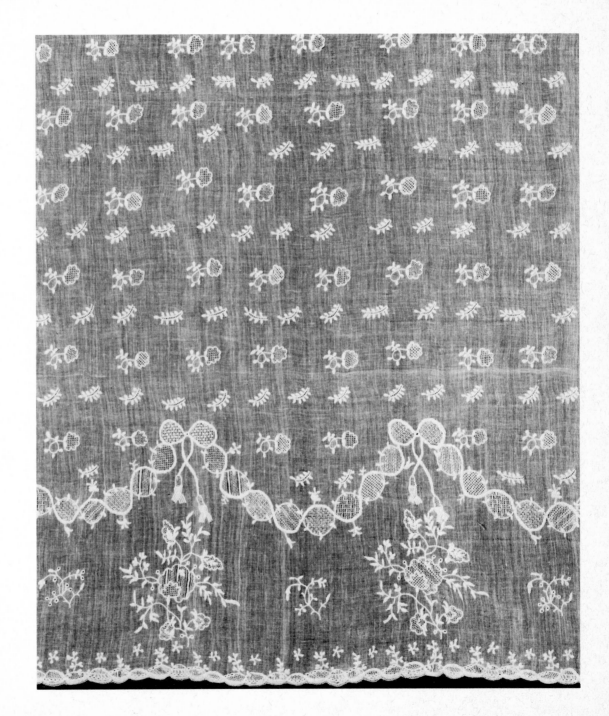

89

Detail of apron, page 89.

81. Waistcoat

18th century, second quarter
Acc. no. 920.35.4. Neg. no. 71TEX96
L. 83.8 cm

Fine white cotton tabby embroidered with white 2-ply linen in back stitch.

The embroidery is worked through two layers of cotton. The design is a linear border pattern with repeating scrolling foliage, flowers, palmettes and tassels in cord quilting with cotton cords. The borders extend down the fronts and across the bottom. There is also embroidery around the spaces for pocket flaps.

The waistcoat has been made up, without pockets and only one flap, in the second half of the 19th century. There is some machine stitching.

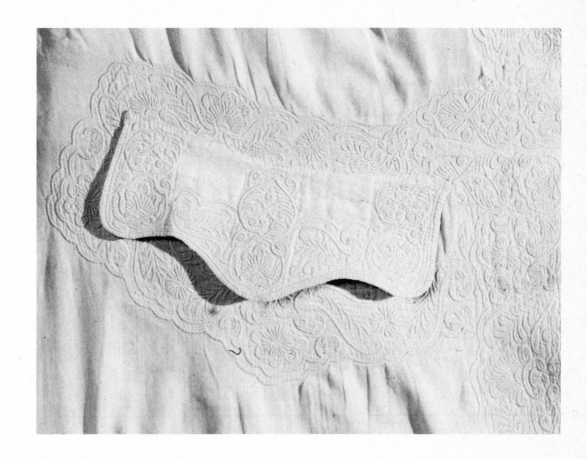

Embroidery Equipment

The fabrics and yarns in 17th and 18th century English embroidery are well represented in this collection. All have been mentioned in the descriptive notes but it may be helpful to readers to give a short review here. Linen and silk were most widely employed as ground fabrics. Little embroidery worked on wool has survived except samplers on tammy cloth and they have often suffered the ravages of moth and damp. Fine linen tabby was much used for work in free stitches such as chain, back, and satin stitches. A slightly coarser tabby with evenly balanced warps and wefts was an ideal ground for embroidery stitches worked to the counted thread, and a coarser kind, canvas, for solid embroidery of the petit and gros point types. Other weaves such as twills, which have an uneven surface, were not often used. An unusual example in the collection is a set of bedcurtains, Plate 41, which is worked on a linen weft satin which looks like a twill. On the other hand silk satin, with its smooth surface and glistening sheen, was the favoured weave particularly for embroideries worked with silk floss, in satin and related stitches, since they showed threads to the best advantage. Other kinds of silk were also used. A tabby similar to taffeta sometimes occurs and the group of decorative aprons of the first half of the 18th century are all worked on a tabby with a slight rib. Embroideries with a cotton ground appeared in the first half of the 18th century but were more important later in the century when fine muslins were fashionable dress materials. Those of the first half of the century came from India, an example being the cotton twill gown, Plate 50, embroidered with coloured wools.

Mixed fabrics with linen warp and cotton weft appeared in the middle of the 17th century and, in the second half of that century and the first half of the 18th, were almost without exception heavy, firm, fabrics woven in a twill weave, usually, but not always, a 2/1 twill and with the weft almost entirely concealing the warp. Such fabrics were admirably suitable as a ground for furnishing embroideries, notably crewelwork bed curtains.

The silk, wool and linen yarns found in these 17th and 18th century embroideries were nearly always 2-ply threads. The 2-ply silks fall into two groups, loosely plied floss silks, and those with a tighter twist. The floss silks, spun with a 2-ply S twist are Western, probably from Italy and, in the 18th century, France. The more tightly twisted ones resemble those found in some contemporary Chinese silks made for the Western market but are also 2-ply S twist. Chinese 2-ply silks were plied with a Z twist. Most of the wools were fine 2-ply long staple worsteds called *crewels* but 3- and 4-ply yarns were also used in canvas and the so-called crewelwork. They, and the linen threads employed mostly for white work, were of domestic manufacture. Both were of course handspun. Wool was basic to the English economy and easy to obtain but skilled spinners of flax for embroidery were sought after, flax being more difficult to spin than wool.

Many fancy yarns and metal threads were employed. Chenille was popular in the 18th century, and silver and silver gilt filé and frisé and metal spirals called purl occur in embroideries in both the 17th and 18th centuries, applied by couching. These threads either came from Europe or were domestic.

Needles made of bronze wire were superseded by steel needles imported into England in the 16th century from Europe where they had been manufactured since the second half of the 14th century. It was not until the 17th century that the manufacture of steel needles was established in England. The Worshipful Company of Needlemakers were granted their charter in 1656 and it is significant that in 1669 the importation of foreign needles into England was prohibited.

An important piece of embroidery equipment was the embroidery frame or tent, to give it its earlier name. Small wooden frames could be held on the knee; very large ones, resembling quilting frames, were supported on trestles, but the most handsome ones were built with stands of the fine woods used for cabinet making and had beautifully turned legs, either a single one or one at each end. All types were adjustable and could be tightened or loosened at will. They were usually rectangular. Round frames which looked rather like a tambour drum were also used and from them the term tambour work, a hooked chain stitch, which had to be done on a stretched fabric, was derived. There are no 18th century examples of this stitch in the collection. It seems to have been more popular in France than in England.

Many embroidresses today strive to find fabrics and yarns with which they can work embroideries copied from those of the 17th and 18th centuries. Both are becoming increasingly difficult to find, but the embroideries remain to serve as inspiration for 20th century interpretation.

Selected Bibliography

Christie, Mrs. Archibald
Samplers and Stitches, B. T. Batsford Ltd., London, England 1948, 4th ed.

Colby, Averil
Quilting, B. T. Batsford Ltd., London, England, 1971.

Colby, Averil
Samplers, B. T. Batsford Ltd., London, England, 1964.

Hackenbroch, Y.
English and other Needlework, Tapestries, and Textiles in the Untermeyer Collection, Thames and Hudson, London, England, 1960.

Jourdain, M.
English Secular Embroidery, Kegan Paul, Trench, Trubner and Co. Ltd., London, England, 1910

King, Donald
Samplers, Victoria and Albert Museum, London, England, 1960.

Nevinson, J. L.
Catalogue of English Domestic Embroidery of the 16th and 17th Centuries, Victoria and Albert Museum, London, England, 1950, 2nd ed.

Swain, Margaret H.
Historical Needlework, A Study in Influence in Scotland and Northern England. Charles Scribner's Sons, New York, 1970.

Wade, N. V.
Basic Stitches of Embroidery, Victoria and Albert Museum, London, England, 1966, 2nd ed.

Wardle, Patricia
Guide to English Embroidery, Victoria and Albert Museum, London, England, 1970.

Wingfield, Digby G. F.
Elizabethan Embroidery, Thomas Yoseloff, New York, 1964.

Stitch Identification and Samples
by Charlotte F. Zuppinger

The stitches illustrated here are those most often found in English embroideries of the periods and kinds covered by this book. It is hoped that those reading the catalogue descriptions of the pieces in the collection will turn to these pages for reference. Unfortunately it has not been possible to show every stage of each stitch, but there are books which will be particularly helpful in the bibliography. Mrs. Christie: *Samplers and Stitches* has been the source most frequently referred to in our researches.

(1)   Chain stitch—front
(2)   Chain stitch—back
(3)   Detached chain stitch

(4)   Double plait stitch—front
(5)   Double plait stitch—back

(6)   Van Dyke stitch—front
(7)   Van Dyke stitch—back

(8)   Coral stitch—front
(9)   Coral stitch—back

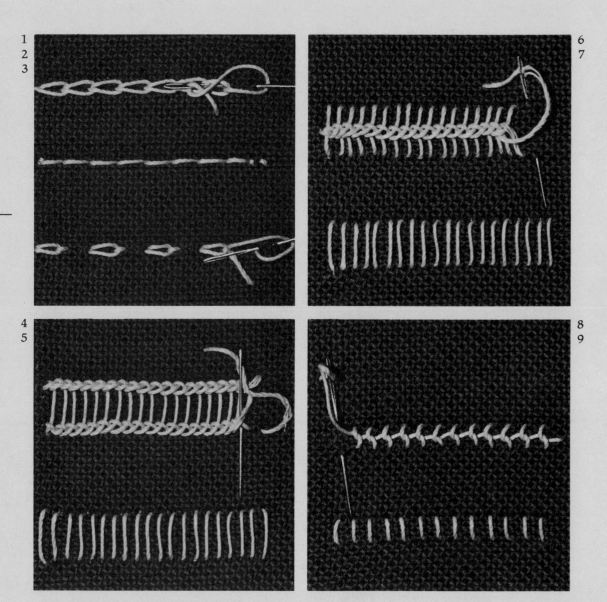

(10) Buttonhole stitch—front
(11) Buttonhole stitch—back
(12) Buttonhole stitch—filling

(13) Cretan stitch—front
(14) Cretan stitch—back

(15) Couching
(16) and (17) Different couching patterns

(18) French knot—front
(19) French knot—back

10
11
12

15
16
17

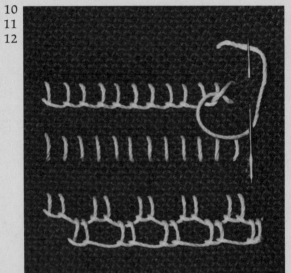

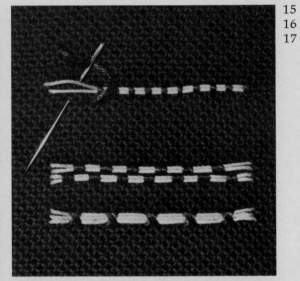

13
14

18
19

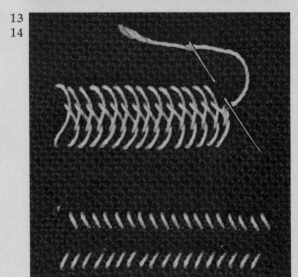

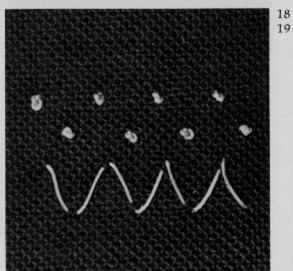

(20) Satin stitch—front
(21) Satin stitch—back

(22) Surface satin stitch—front
(23) Surface satin stitch—back

(24) Geometrical satin stitch
(25) Geometrical satin stitch

(26) Long and short stitch
(27) Long and short stitch

20
21
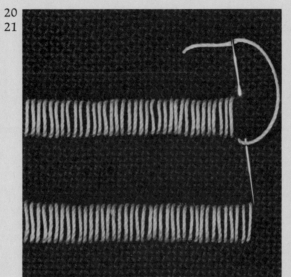

24
25
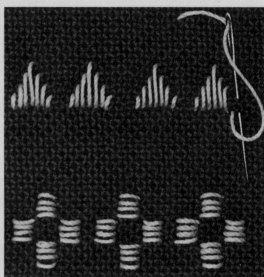

22
23
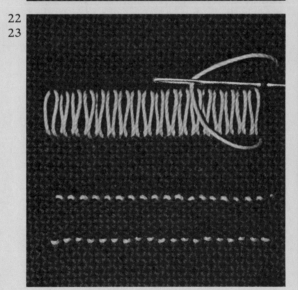

26
27
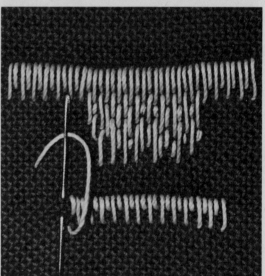

(28) Roumanian stitch—front
(29) Roumanian stitch—back

(30) Brick stitch—front
(31) Brick stitch—back

(32) Stem stitch—front
(33) Stem stitch—back
(34) Stem stitch—filling

(35) Running stitch
(36) Double threaded running stitch
(37) Back stitch
(38) Double back stitch—
(left) back, (right) front

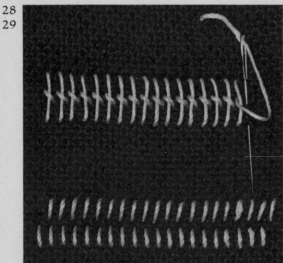

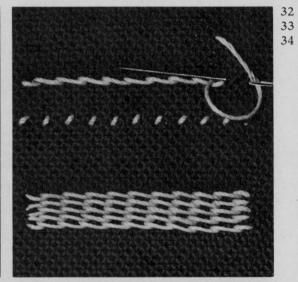

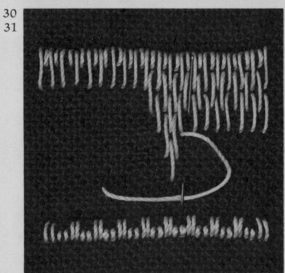

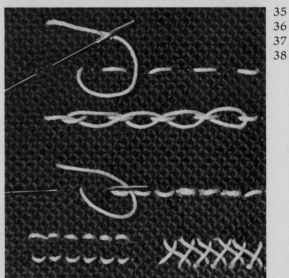

Canvas Stitches

(1)   Cross-stitch—front
(2)   Cross-stitch—back

(3)   Marking cross-stitch—front
(4)   Marking cross-stitch—back

(5)   Long Armed cross-stitch—front
(6)   Long Armed cross-stitch—back

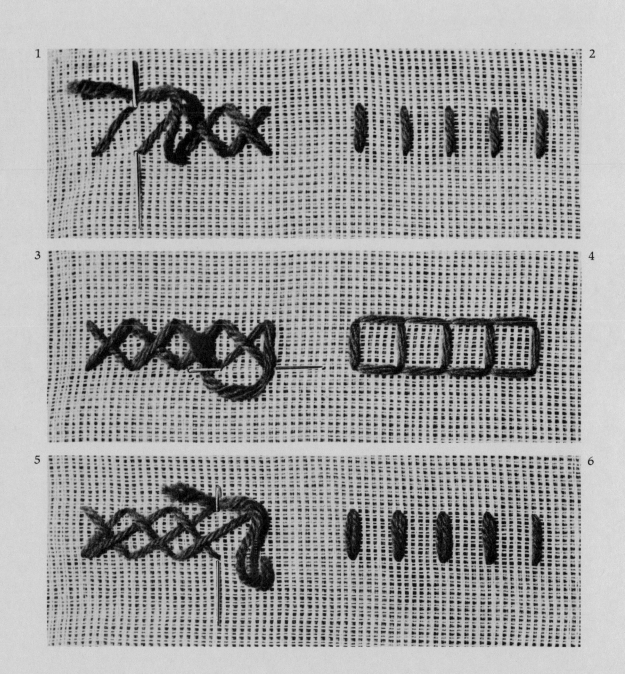

(7) Two sided Italian cross-stitch—in progress
(8) Two sided Italian cross-stitch—completed

(9) Double cross-stitch—front
(10) Double cross-stitch—back

(11) Tent stitch—front
(12) Tent stitch—back

(13) Plaited Gobelin stitch—front
(14) Plaited Gobelin stitch—back

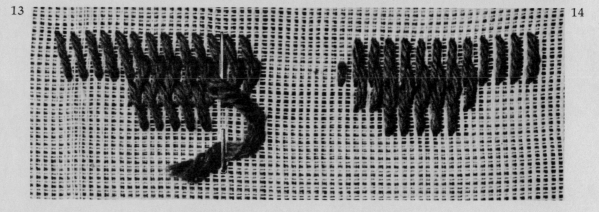

(15) Crosslet-stitch—front
(16) Crosslet-stitch—back

(17) Florentine stitch—front
(18) Florentine stitch—back

(19) Hungarian stitch—front
(20) Hungarian stitch—back

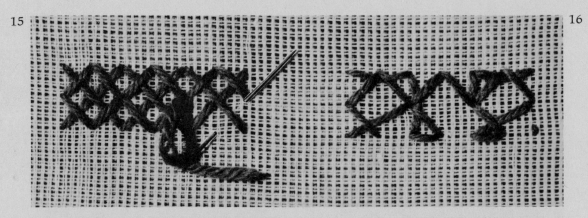

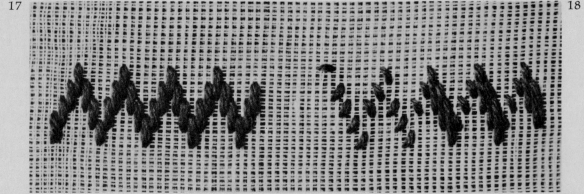